Publication of this book was generously supported by:

Major sponsors

The Engineering Council (WISE - Women Into Science and Engineering)

The Department of Trade and Industry (Development Unit for Women in SET, Office of Science and Technology)

Engineering and Marine Training Authority (EMTA)

Other sponsors

The Wellcome Trust

The Association of the British Pharmaceutical Industry (ABPI)

Engineering Employers' Federation (EEF)

Executive committee

Chair: Dr Nancy J. Lane OBE (Department of Zoology, University of Cambridge)

Ann Bailey (Head of Education and Training Affairs, EEF)

Marie-Noëlle Barton (Manager – WISE Campaign, The Engineering Council)

Professor Judith A.K. Howard CBE (Department of Chemistry, University of Durham)

Dr Joan Mason (Chair, Association for Women in Science and Engineering)

Judith May (formerly Senior Editor in Biology, Oxford University Press)

Dr Caroline Roberts (Head, Development Unit for Women in SET, Office of Science and Technology, Department of Trade and Industry)

Lynda Sharp (formerly Head, Development Unit for Women in SET, Office of Science and Technology, Department of Trade and Industry)

Libby Steele (Education and Training Executive, The Association of the British Pharmaceutical Industry)

Josephine Warrior (Writer)

Janet Whitaker (formerly Head of Sex Equality Branch, and Equal Opportunities Consultant)

Other advisers

Dr Mary Phillips (Programme Manager, The Wellcome Trust)

Dr Lily M. Segerman-Peck

Dr Anne Wright CBE DL (Vice-Chancellor, University of Sunderland)

The Daphne Jackson Memorial Fellowships Trust

Foreword

By the Right Honourable Margaret Beckett MP, President of The Board of Trade

Women are a growing force within science, engineering and technology (SET) but, outside the medical and life sciences they are often still in the minority in their individual workplaces. In all areas they can face obstacles in trying to combine a career and a family, and hit the same glass ceiling which affects many women professionals. This handbook looks at the experiences of women who have survived and succeeded in SET, and provides positive guidance to those embarking on or re-launching their careers.

I know from my own experience as a metallurgist, and from the experiences of female friends who are working in SET, that the workplace can still be a hard one for women. Being in a minority can be a very lonely existence for some, and it also means that there are few role models around to provide inspiration. Women don't necessarily need or want the company and advice of other women all the time; indeed, some find it extremely challenging and rewarding to make a successful career in a field that is still largely male dominated. However, I expect that most would acknowledge that the challenges are sometimes rather wearing, and would welcome the timely advice or comradeship from those who have faced similar problems before.

I warmly welcome this book. It is a mine of invaluable information and advice of the 'how to do it' type - how to plan a career, how to increase one's chances of getting a particular job or research contract, how to benefit from networking and mentoring, how to get back to work after a career break, and so on. It also provides extremely useful information relevant to the many women who want to combine a career in SET with having a family. I particularly commend the profiles of the women who are succeeding in a diverse range of SET sectors. These not only give an insight into how these women are managing to progress and overcome obstacles, but also convey a tangible sense of enthusiasm for their jobs. I am sure that these profiles alone will provide valuable inspiration for any readers who perhaps feel ground down with the pressures of their own careers.

I also welcome this book as President of The Board of Trade, because I think it will do much to support and encourage, and therefore retain, women working in SET. The fact that women are still generally under-represented in these sectors is, of course, disadvantageous for the United Kingdom's competitiveness. We need to promote a balanced workforce to ensure that the talents that women can provide are utilised to the full. I see this book as providing a valuable contribution towards that aim, and hope that it will be of real benefit and inspiration, not only to women as individuals, but also to the employers and potential employers of women in all sectors of science, engineering and technology.

Margaret Beckett

Contents

Can this book help you?

Can this book help you?

- Are you considering a career in science, engineering and technology (SET)?
- Are you an SET graduate trying to obtain your first position after doing a degree?
- Have you started work in an SET environment and want to know how to increase your skills and abilities in order to advance your career?
- Are you in your early 30s, and feel that your career is stuck in a rut?
- Or are you thinking about taking a career break, or trying to get back into SET after taking one?
- Or have you reached a position in your career where you have achieved a certain amount and are beginning to wonder what to do next?

Cracking it! is for anybody and everybody involved in SET. While it is aimed specifically at women, the information this book contains will be equally useful to many men. Similarly, it does not focus on a particular sector, but aims to indicate the range and variety of career routes that are possible if you have a background in science, engineering and technology. It is wide-ranging in scope, as the following chapter summary shows.

- **Chapter 1, Ladders and snakes: creating your career**, provides an introduction to the career pathways in science, engineering and technology (SET) and describes how you can create a career for yourself in a constantly changing world. It also discusses the concept of the glass ceiling, and how women have overcome barriers to success.
- **Chapter 2, Almonds into peaches: education, training and lifelong learning**, summarises the various skills, qualifications, courses, and funding sources that you might want to bring into play for yourself or your staff.
- **Chapter 3, The great race: getting the right job**, outlines the points you need to consider when preparing your CVs, filling in application forms, and constructing effective letters of application. It also discusses the different types of interviews, questions and assessment procedures that you might encounter.
- **Chapter 4, A helping hand: mentoring and networking**, reveals how effective mentoring and successful networking can make all the difference to your career and covers these concepts in detail.
- **Chapter 5, Having it all? balancing career and family responsibilities**, discusses the problem that many women face: how do you manage your work, your career development and your family responsibilities? It identifies the issues you may want to think about, some of the possible solutions, and outlines the ways in which various problems can be overcome.

- **Chapter 6, The water's cold: returning after a career break**, tackles the strategies of managing a career break successfully and shows that it is possible to get back into SET after several years away.

- **Chapter 7, Academic research: a long-term future on a short-term contract?** sets out the advantages and disadvantages of academic, short-term contracts and focuses on what you need to think about when considering this career route.

- **Chapter 8, All change? branching out**, gives examples of the many ways in which you can use your SET expertise in areas other than a straightforward scientific, engineering or technological career. Publishing, teaching and the law are some of the possibilities.

- And **Chapter 9, Are we being heard? involvement in public life**, looks at the ways in which your skills and expertise can benefit the wider community. It describes some of the opportunities that are available and what you yourself might gain by taking an increased role in public life.

Most of the chapters contain a mixture of information, checklists, suggested strategies and action plans. The points raised are illustrated by quotes from people in SET, the vast majority of them women. **Further Reading** is suggested at the end of each chapter, and many of the titles should be obtainable through your library. A list of **Acronyms** is given at the end of the book, as well as a list of **Useful Addresses**.

To highlight the issues raised in the text, *Cracking it!* also contains over 20 longer profiles of women in the various sectors of science, engineering and technology who are in the process of doing just that! There are many highly successful women in SET, but once again these profiles aim to encompass a range of individuals, from young graduates to grandmothers, and to describe their careers in a variety of sectors and at different stages.

The profiles range from the descriptive to the informative to the inspirational, but they all have one common thread. The sentence that came up – without exception – in every interview was a short and a simple one.

'I enjoy my work.'

Cracking it! aims to help you enjoy yours.

1

Ladders and snakes: creating your career

'Science has a wonderful range of opportunities and so much is happening. It's absorbing and challenging – I'm never bored.' Materials scientist

The advantages of working in science, engineering and technology (SET) are impressive:

- you will be working in an exciting growth area of the international economy
- with the right skills, qualifications and experience you will be highly employable and there are jobs at all levels
- you can earn a decent salary almost anywhere in the world
- you will have a series of fascinating opportunities ahead of you, whether you want to travel, to contribute to the knowledge base of the next century, or to improve living conditions and solve some of the problems of society.

So why don't more women choose to enter and stay in SET?

The answers are many and varied, and have been thoughtfully discussed in a series of articles and books published over the last decade or so. (Several of the more recent titles are suggested in the Further Reading section on page 18.) Some of the factors that seem to emerge include the way science is taught, the preconceptions and stereotypes held by girls and boys and men and women about the nature of work in SET, the lack of role models and, in the past, the negative attitudes of some employers to employing women – although this has changed radically in recent years.

This book is not intended to add to that debate, interesting and important though it is, but to demonstrate the interest and rewards that a career in science, engineering or technology can hold for women – as well as for men! It uses case studies of real women in different sectors of SET at different stages in their careers to show not how it *should* be done, but ways in which it *has* been done. It is not a theoretical blueprint which lays down ten immediate rules for guaranteed success, but a thoroughly practical handbook which is designed to provide you with a toolkit of ideas and information, strategies and action plans, from which you can pick and choose, and all of which are intended to help you to create a satisfying career for yourself in science, engineering or technology.

But these days creating a career for yourself in any area is easier said than done, so where do you start?

Up the ladder

In the past, it may not have been easier, but it was more straightforward. In many professions there was – and in many professions there still is – what might be called a classical or conventional career route. While there is no single 'correct' route, and obviously different 'rungs' of the ladder have varying titles from company to company and university to university, the main thrust behind such a career route usually involves you starting at or near the bottom and working your way upwards, sometimes changing employer as you advance.

The diagrams show some examples of how such a career route might work.

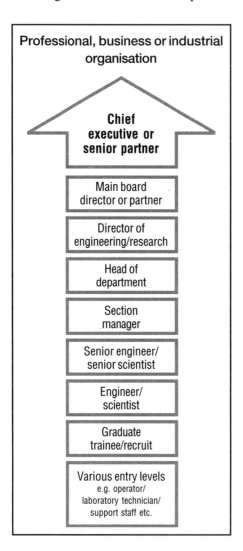

Professional, business or industrial organisation

Chief executive or senior partner

Main board director or partner

Director of engineering/research

Head of department

Section manager

Senior engineer/ senior scientist

Engineer/ scientist

Graduate trainee/recruit

Various entry levels
e.g. operator/ laboratory technician/ support staff etc.

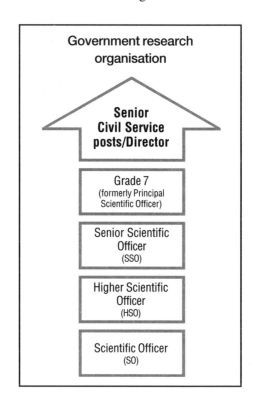

Government research organisation

Senior Civil Service posts/Director

Grade 7
(formerly Principal Scientific Officer)

Senior Scientific Officer
(SSO)

Higher Scientific Officer
(HSO)

Scientific Officer
(SO)

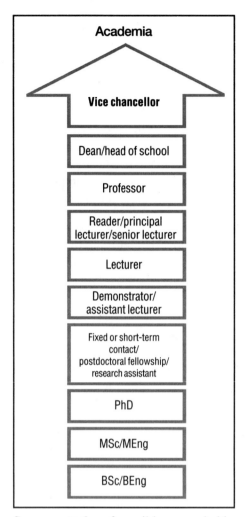

Some examples of possible career ladders.

This 'ladder' model of a career route has advantages. And disadvantages. The main issue for most women (and many men) has been that it is difficult to move up from the lower rungs of the ladder. Often, even when you do move up, you get so far and no further – hitting the so-called glass ceiling (see page 8). Advancing in your career can be especially difficult if you want or need a career break or period of part-time working to be an active parent of young children. Sometimes reaching the top of the career ladder means moving out of scientific and technical positions and into management or administration. If you do not want to do this, preferring to continue with research, for example, then formal promotion opportunities may be more limited.

At the same time, in many academic and research spheres a great deal of career satisfaction can come not only from having a senior position, but also from earning an international reputation, being awarded significant funding, and being part of a world-class laboratory or research group. Accordingly the idea of 'promotion' needs to be used cautiously in these contexts.

Today even in those organisations and professions where there is still a form of 'career ladder', there tends to be an increased degree of flexibility, more sideways movement and, ideally, a greater openness. When you are considering working for a company with this sort of structure, you might want to find out from its recruitment literature and company reports the percentage distribution of the sexes within the different levels – does it have any women in senior positions or on the board, for example? – and, if possible, how long it took them to get there. If you are aiming at an academic environment, perhaps an idea of the representation of women in permanent and senior positions will enable you to assess the opportunities that might open up later on.

However, the principal disadvantage of this 'up the ladder' career route for many people is quite simple: it may no longer exist, or, when it does, you may find that the ladder is kicked out from under you.

So how do you cope?

Out of the window and up the drainpipe

'Many had unusual career patterns – only a few had travelled the main staircase route; others had gone out of the window and up the drainpipe. I suppose if you have to avoid glass ceilings, even subconsciously, that is not so surprising.' Helena Kennedy, Beyond the Glass Ceiling, 1996, page 7

Whereas once you might have 'planned' your career, now you have to 'create' it, and these days the image of a career ladder could be replaced by that of a less dignified (but more individual) drainpipe, or the idea of a patchwork quilt where you design your career individually, working outwards from the central core of qualifications and skills that you have, and where you can develop and vary the design to make the most of the individual 'materials' you acquire and the space you have available to work within.

Creating your own career is a challenging concept. It means:

- thinking flexibly and in terms of a 'fluid' career timeline, rather than sticking rigidly to plans that may go out of date
- building on your accomplishments, committing yourself to continuous or 'lifelong' learning, and constantly developing your range of personal transferable skills and breadth of experience so that you are in a position to take advantage of specific opportunities as and when they occur
- moving across academic disciplines, business functions and countries where and when necessary to get a wider perspective
- sometimes working at interfaces, for instance, between the skills and disciplines, or between industry and academia, and developing the ability to make interconnections

- seeking out unusual or niche opportunities, and exploiting them
- accepting that career security will reside in your own talents and your ability to 'package' and market them effectively, and that it is up to you to make the most of what you have to offer (the idea of 'portfolio working' comes in here, and this is discussed in more detail on page 179)
- taking responsibility for your own career development, and making it happen, rather than letting someone else decide your future.

This can be an exciting prospect. Yes, it may involve risk-taking, but if you are trained in a scientific, engineering or technological field, you are better equipped than most to explore and enjoy the challenges.

... But what about the snakes?

Even the most carefully laid career plans can be disrupted. Setbacks can come out of the blue or may follow uncontrollable global, national or economic changes. Discrimination – whether because of age, race, gender or disability – is, sadly, still a fact of working life which you may be forced to confront. While you can aspire to creating your own career, work must accommodate external realities and they are, often, unforgiving.

'Careers most frequently result from earlier decisions which result in a narrowing range of opportunities. Career choices are also obviously limited by economic recession or increased by economic prosperity. Careers can result from coincidences and chance encounters, from family connections and the ties of friendship, as well as from organizational restructurings and changes in economic conditions.' Julia Evetts, Gender and Career in Science and Engineering, 1996, page 50

While *Cracking it!* does not outline specific actions to overcome particular types of discrimination – such as racial prejudice or discrimination against those with a disability – the information and strategies are intended to assist anyone and everyone wishing to work in SET, whatever their individual circumstances. Most forward-looking employers will now have a statement of good practice for equal opportunities. However, when you are considering whether to work for an organisation, what you need to know is how that statement is translated into effective practice, and how that practice is then evaluated.

- Are recruitment and promotion procedures regularly reviewed to avoid discrimination?
- Are equal opportunity statements formulated into targets which can be regularly appraised by managers?
- Is there some form of mentoring or careers advice for employees? (For more information on mentoring, see Chapter 4.)

The message that this book aims to convey is that while you can't prevent setbacks – and sometimes you can't even prepare for them – you can overcome them.

But first you need to know what you're up against. And one of the main obstacles that women, in particular, may face, is the glass ceiling.

Cracking the glass ceiling

'Just at this moment her head struck against the roof of the hall: in fact she was now rather more than nine feet high, and she at once took up the little golden key and hurried off to the garden door. Poor Alice! It was as much as she could do, lying down on one side, to look through into the beautiful garden with one eye; but to get through was more hopeless than ever.' Lewis Carroll, Alice's Adventures in Wonderland, 1865

The concept of the 'glass ceiling' as an invisible barrier which allows women to see into the upper reaches but prevents them from getting there, has been around for some time. Several books have been written on the subject, and published statistics certainly demonstrate that as far as women are concerned, it is a case of 'the higher the fewer'. This is true in both academia and business, as the following quote reveals: 'Women's representation in management has slowly increased in the past two decades but women at the very top are scarcely visible ... Women are very poorly represented as both executive and non-executive directors ... the proportion of women in senior academic posts is derisory ... The situation is especially disturbing at Oxford and Cambridge where the number of women Professors and Fellows remains tiny.' *The Report of The Hansard Society Commission on Women at the Top*, 1990, pages 8–10

Five years later the follow-up report concludes: 'Certainly there has been some progress, though no-one would wish to claim it has been spectacular ... There is as yet, however, no room for relaxation.' *Women at the Top: progress after five years*, 1996, pages 3 and 19

This conclusion is supported by others:

- ' ... there is some indication that even employed in similar positions with similar experience there is a trend for women to be paid less than men and also that women are not reaching the highest rungs of the ladder at the same rate as men.' *The Ivanhoe Guide to Chartered Patent Agents 1997*, page 97

- 'At present it would be easier for women to land on the moon than for them to land in the boardroom of a major British engineering company.' Malcolm Wicks, MP, at the 1997 WISE (Women Into Science and Engineering) conference

- 'Occupational segregation and the persistence of the glass ceiling mean that women's pay is, on average, only 80 per cent of men's.' Women's National Commission (WNC), *Women in the 90s*, 1994, page 7

But how do women themselves view the existence of the glass ceiling?

The women profiled throughout this book are almost all engaged in careers in SET, areas that in the past have been considered traditionally male. Some of the scientists and engineers in this book feel they have not reached the glass ceiling; some believe they have hit it, and some might say they have broken through it. Here is a selection of their comments.

- 'Well. It does exist, but it's very difficult to pinpoint it or to try to work against it.' Research manager
- 'Many women blame the glass ceiling when really they're lacking the team or interpersonal skills they need to progress further.' Project manager
- 'It must exist because women haven't got the network that the men have got for a start.' Research chemist
- 'The glass ceiling is there but it is not always deliberately applied.' Research zoologist
- 'It's easy to get into management; impossible to get on the board.' IT consultant
- 'I don't think there is a glass ceiling but I do think women set limits to their own progress. Usually their families are their first priority. Men are less constrained, but women do set their own constraints.' Civil engineer
- 'The glass ceiling is quite a difficult concept. I think in the engineering industry there are unverbalised perceptions. There are very few women at senior level because of the underlying assumptions. But it's changing.' Electrical engineer

Two women on the verge of top management epitomise the differing approaches:

'I'm at a stage in my career [mid 40s] where I'm considering my next move. I think I could break through the glass ceiling, but I haven't yet decided whether I want to. The job would be extremely demanding, and there are other areas of my life I want to develop.' Government scientist

'I realise now that what I want to do next is become managing director of a similar company to the one I am working in. I've just seen a former female colleague make that move. If she can do it, I can do it.' Senior computer consultant

The career profiles throughout this book are not intended to either prove or disprove the continuing existence of a glass ceiling, but they do provide evidence that if it does exist, it is possible to break through it.

Success factors – or getting into the 'beautiful garden'

Arguably the solution to both increasing the number of women working in SET and improving the conditions for them is the 'critical mass' argument.

- 'The single most important trend that creates, improves, and supports opportunities for women in the physical sciences is the presence of other successful women in the field. Increasing the number of women in science decreases the solitude of the struggle. Most importantly, the infrastructure necessary to support women in science will not be built without a representative number of women in the field.' National Science Foundation. *Women and Science: celebrating achievements, charting challenges. Conference Report, March 1997*, page 2 (accessible on website: http://www.ehr.nsf.gov/conferences/women95.htm)

This then, begs the question of what enables some women to have an exciting and rewarding career in SET, while other women seem to reach a plateau and go no further. Obviously there are as many reasons for success as there are successful women, but during the interviews for the profiles in this book, certain themes emerged.

Scientific and technical knowledge and expertise

This goes without saying: you have to have mastered the technical skills and knowledge required for your job. The rest of this book is based on the assumption that you will have the expertise that your work demands.

Transferable skills

Scientific and technical expertise is a prerequisite for any career in SET, but transferable skills are equally important. Transferable skills include such competences as numeracy, literacy, IT experience, interpersonal and especially communication skills, teamworking, project management, problem-solving and financial control. These are discussed in detail on page 22, but they are mentioned here because many women felt that it was their transferable skills that had made the difference at critical points in their careers.

- 'The development of transferable skills is crucial. How about budgeting, teamworking and strategic thinking? Can you handle meetings? Do you know how to deal with an aggressive colleague? Identify what you are lacking, and then do something about it.' Civil engineer

Good verbal and written communication skills are particularly important.

- 'I never used to listen: I used to tell people what *I* thought. Now I've realised how much I can learn from others. Now I ask them what they think.' Project manager

- 'I'm persuasive. I can get people to take risks.' Biophysicist
- 'I am able to explain things between disciplines without alienating people.' Business systems manager

Networking

Networking is crucial, and so a whole chapter is devoted to this issue (Chapter 4). Here let the following piece of advice, allied to networking, suffice:

- 'Don't make enemies. You don't have to make friends with everybody, but you do need to foster good working relationships with as many people as possible in as many places as possible. Initially I felt very negative towards a man from outside the company who got the job I wanted, but I worked at cultivating a professional relationship with him. It was just as well I did because six months later his old boss became the new managing director.' Industrial chemist

Visibility

As a woman in SET you are in a minority which means you have 'greater visibility'. This can work 'both ways', but successful women make it work *for* them.

- 'Visibility has been a factor. It means your mistakes stand out more, but so do your successes.' Systems analyst
- 'Visibility is important – it's not enough to be doing – you have to be seen to be doing. Make sure you "sign your work" and obtain your fair share of credit for grant proposals, papers and poster presentations.' Research chemist

Luck

There can be no doubt that luck does play a significant part in successful careers and particularly in SET where you are so very often dealing with or exploring the unknown.

- 'Luck – being in the right place at the right time or coming up with the right idea or right approach or even having the right boss and the right partner! – should not be denied ... '

but:

- ' ... you also have to get yourself into a position where you can take advantage of good luck and, conversely, overcome the disadvantage of bad luck.' Microbiologist

Making and identifying opportunities

'We're not looking at males and females. We're looking at people, engineering people. And there are not enough of them.' Susan McRae et al., Women into Engineering and Science: Employers' policies and practices, 1991, page 34

When opportunities are thin on the ground, try to invent your own job or make yourself indispensable, perhaps by taking a job related to the one you really want even though the salary may be low, for a limited period.

At other times, train yourself to recognise an opportunity: a type of technology that is about to take off, a niche area of science that you can enjoy and exploit, a new growth field that is attracting funding, or some other set of factors that might justify a change of direction.

- 'I managed to ride the crest of an opportunity wave. It was the right time for advances in magnetic resonance: the technology was in place and the money was available. Earlier the techniques would not have been at the right stage of development; later the money would probably have been tighter. I was very fortunate, but I also made sure that I took full advantage of my good fortune.' Chemical engineer

Current more general opportunities include:

- the growth of interdisciplinary subjects, which can be a great opportunity for people who are good at seeing connections and communicating
- the international demand for scientists, engineers and technologists.

Developing a positive self-image

'Too many women don't apply for promotion. They haven't got the confidence. If a man fulfils half the criteria of the job spec he might apply, believing he's halfway there. A woman will focus on the requirements she hasn't got.' Personnel officer

Even successful women can lack confidence and be over-critical about their abilities. How can you change your own self-perception and start seeing your 'jug' as half full instead of half empty?

Many women find it easier to 'measure' themselves by external factors such as qualifications and structured appraisals and thrive best in an environment where success can be quantified in 'formal' terms. If you fall into this category, recognise this, and bear it in mind when you are changing work environments. However, try to shift your perspective so that you can also recognise other 'standards' of achievement.

One way to build up your confidence is to put yourself in a situation where you have the possibility of achieving something difficult.

- 'During my PhD I trained as a commercial diver – it was the toughest thing I have ever done. You are in the pitchblack at 30m depth, petrified and freezing. You are not floating around, you are working – putting up scaffolding, dismantling well heads. Sticking with it and succeeding did wonders for my confidence in all sorts of ways.' Project manager

Obviously by taking this course of action you are risking failure, and it is important that you give yourself permission to fail at times: a limited amount of failure can be constructive and you can learn as much from it as from your successes. What you will want to avoid, though, is repeating the same mistakes and allowing a lack of success to prevent you from trying again.

Other strategies to enhance your self-confidence are described on page 128.

As you become more positive about your own abilities, this will be reflected in other people's reactions to you. Ironically, success does breed success: 'Once you have established your credibility your reputation goes before you and you find you can achieve what you want to: I even got promoted when I was six months pregnant.' Senior Scientific Officer

Risk-taking

'Only those who will risk going too far can possibly find out how far one can go.'
T. S. Eliot

One of the themes that emerged from the profiles was that successful women in SET have often developed the ability to take risks – something that many women are conditioned against doing from their childhood.

- 'As a girl I was very protected and I think my reluctance to take risks stems from that and my fear of the unknown. My immediate reaction is often to say "no", but slowly I've learned to get into the habit of "buying" myself some time to think about my answer.' Production manager
- 'I like the American way of thinking: if you haven't failed, you haven't tried.' Assistant IT consultant
- 'I realised early on that I would have to establish and continually reinforce my credibility, and to take risks. I did both these things. When you have to *do* something you learn – I only started using a PC when I was 40.' Telecommunications consultant
- 'The Chinese say: "The longest journey begins with a single step." I've discovered that you can go a long way, one step at a time.' Aerospace engineer

The first step

Before you can work out where you want to go, you need to analyse where you're at. Many businesses identify their current position by doing a SWOT analysis, listing their Strengths, Weaknesses, Opportunities and Threats in a chart format. You may find it useful to draw up your own personal SWOT analysis.

What are your **strengths?**

> What are your qualifications?
>
> Which personal transferable skills do you have?
>
> What experience can you offer?
>
> Then look at this another way: what *benefits* does your employer get from employing *you* rather than somebody else?

Next consider your **weaknesses** (except that you don't have 'weaknesses' any more, just 'development areas').

> What's limiting you?
>
> What's holding you back?
>
> What can you do about it – in the short term?
>
> – in the longer term?
>
> Can you look at any of those weaknesses in another way and turn them into a strength?

Now work out the **opportunities** that are available to you.

> What are your current and future opportunities?
>
> List them in order of desirability.
>
> Re-read the section on making and identifying opportunities (page 12).
>
> Is there anything more you can add to the list?
>
> Work out the advantages and disadvantages of the opportunities that most appeal to you.

Finally are there any **threats** which are restricting your choices?

> Are there any ways in which you can minimise or circumvent those threats?

Doing a SWOT analysis at regular intervals throughout your working life will help you to see where you have come from, where you are, and where you might go.

Action planning

'Until you decide what you want out of life and out of a career, you're going to drift. Once you decide what you want, you have your direction and then you can plan and implement.' Technical operations manager

Action planning can help you take control of your career. Action planning involves:

- working out where you are now
- deciding on what you want to achieve
- working out a way to achieve it
- putting your plan into operation
- monitoring the progress you are making
- reflecting, reviewing and following-up at specific intervals.

Your action plan might not succeed, or halfway through it you might scrap it for a different one or need to adapt it to meet new circumstances, but this does not negate its usefulness. Action plans are a means to an end, and you may have different actions plans for different aspects of your life and career. The ones suggested throughout *Cracking it!* are designed to be used as 'springboards' to help you formulate specific strategies that meet your individual needs.

Action Plan: Taking control

Try working through this brief action plan now and start to take control of your own career development.

- ❑ Where are you now?
- ❑ Where do you really want to go next?
- ❑ What's the route you need to follow to get there?
- ❑ What's the first step you need to take?
- ❑ **When are you going to take that step?**

If you're still unsure about where you go from here, why not start by reading the rest of this book?

Maureen Donnelly, principal telecommunications consultant

Maureen Donnelly's career path has encompassed working for a large organisation with a traditional 'career ladder' structure, combining motherhood with a senior technical management role, self-employment, and working for a dynamic young telecommunications consultancy. She is now in her mid 40s.

You could say I've 'done' my career the wrong way round.

I think the traditional scientific career path in industry is to get a job with a small company after doing a degree, work for them for three to four years and acquire a wide range of skills and experience. Then many people go into consultancy for a spell: the diversity of the clients further hones their technical and business expertise. After that, they might be headhunted by a large company and rise to a senior position by the time they're in their mid 40s.

That's not how it has worked out for me.

After a BSc in Applied Mathematics and Physics at Queen's University, Belfast, I joined the telecommunications part of what was then the Post Office in London as a fast-stream graduate entrant. I was one of only a handful of women recruited along with about 50 men.

I originally intended to stay at BT for a couple of years but I was there for nearly 20, because my work evolved along with the world of telecommunications itself. By the time I left I was dealing with new products and services created by advances in technology, and national pricing strategies to enable the company to compete in an international marketplace.

I stayed with the one company for so long because I was promoted every three or four years – always into an interesting new area with work that was technically challenging, and always with more money and status. I could have stayed at BT but after 18 years I started thinking about leaving. There were a number of factors in my decision-making. BT had all the advantages of a big company – an excellent salary and working conditions, a good pension scheme and relative security – but if you only work for one organisation you see the world from a slightly skewed perspective and you can lack a variety of experience. I also realised that organisations were tending to recruit external expertise into senior jobs far more than they had used to. I hadn't actually hit the glass ceiling – I just began to believe that I would, although I have to say that many of my male colleagues felt the same way as I did.

At about this time I became a mother. BT was very good on family-friendly policies and I negotiated coming back part-time initially. I was also able to switch from an operational role to a staff function. This meant that by using live-in helps I was able to continue working at a senior level. However, as the months passed, I found I wanted to spend more time with my son before he started school. I thought being self-employed might enable me to achieve this.

A four-week senior executive programme at the London Business School provided me not only with new contacts and a chance to update a range of skills and knowledge, but also with time out for thinking. After the course, I applied for voluntary redundancy and started my own business.

There were many advantages to working from home. I had built up an excellent network of contacts during my years at BT and was an active member of associations such as the Telecoms Managers Association. This enabled me to obtain various consultancy projects. Interestingly enough, the new contacts I made through organisations like the National Childbirth Trust and the nursery school also proved fruitful, work-wise. Telecommunications involves a lot of teamwork and much of the work was done with other people, so I never felt isolated.

However, at times, it was difficult to manage the flow of work. During one year I had no jobs for two months, and then three bids I'd made for large contracts were all successful and I was working a 70-hour week for months on end. This lifestyle wasn't what I had wanted either. As a result, when I was headhunted by a new telecommunications firm to be their director of marketing and product development, I decided to join them.

I stayed there for two years and then networking played its part once more when I was planning my next move. I approached the MD of Analysys, a telecommunications consultancy, who invited me to visit his company for a 'chat'. The 'chat' turned out to be a full-blown interview where I had personality and numerical tests and was asked to do a presentation to a group of six people on a specific telecoms subject. By lunchtime I had proved I could think on my feet and they asked me when I could start.

I enjoy both the 'technical' aspects and the strategic thinking that are demanded in my current role. I have to be able to understand the very latest telecoms technology: what you can do with it – and what you can't.

The company is young and growing, and I'm one of its oldest employees, as well as the first woman to be appointed at principal level on the consultancy side. This isn't a problem as most of the men I work with now have young families and want to spend time with them. Analysys recognises this and, like a growing number of forward-looking companies, provides a supportive environment which enables us to combine family life with working at the top level in a fast-moving industry.

Women and SET

Gender and Career in Science and Engineering

Julia Evetts, Taylor & Francis, 1996

Written very much from a sociological point of view, this book examines the career experiences of a group of engineers and scientists working for two large industrial companies. The chapters on career routes, dual career families and ways of resolving career issues are enlightening.

Tapping the Talent

Opportunity 2000, 1997

A slim booklet describing some of the reasons why relatively few girls and women enter and stay in SET, and outlining an agenda for action for businesses to increase the talent available to them by encouraging more young women into science, engineering and technology. Obtainable from Opportunity 2000 (see page 108).

Women in Engineering: a good place to be?

Ruth Carter and Gill Kirkup, Macmillan Education, 1990

A good summary of views covering issues such as education, public and private lives, and working for change. Lots of interviews with female engineers both in the UK and the USA, with reference to the situations they encountered and how they dealt with them.

Who Succeeds in Science? The gender dimension

Gerhard Sonnert with the assistance of Gerald Holton, Rutgers University Press, 1995

Interesting career histories of successful American women and men who have stayed in science, and others who have 'branched out'. The authors analyse success factors and aim their suggestions at both 'aspiring scientists' and policy-makers who wish to facilitate scientists' careers.

Making the Most: women in science, engineering and technology, building a workforce for sustained competitiveness

Department of Trade and Industry and Opportunity 2000, 1995

This booklet shows how six of the UK's leading enterprises are *Making the Most* of women specialists, and highlights the business benefits which this is bringing to them. The examples of best practice are from large enterprises – but the principles, policies and practices are equally applicable to smaller and medium-sized ones. Obtainable from Opportunity 2000 (see page 108).

The glass ceiling

Beyond the Glass Ceiling

Sian Griffiths (editor) With an introduction by Helena Kennedy, QC
Manchester University Press in association with The Times Higher Education Supplement, 1996

This book features interviews with 40 women 'whose ideas shape the modern world'. Although not all the women are scientists, engineers or technologists, *Beyond the Glass Ceiling* is good for background reading of an inspirational nature, and demonstrates the many career paths that can be taken, how setbacks can become opportunities, and the varying strategies adopted by women 'who have made it' to deal with issues such as childcare, relationships and promotion.

The Rising Tide: a report on women in science, engineering and technology

HMSO, 1994

Interesting background reading which sets the picture in the UK, analyses the problems, and suggests some ways forward.

Women in Science, Engineering and Technology – Government response to the report, The Rising Tide: women in science, engineering and technology

HMSO, 1994

The official response to the above report.

Shattering the Glass Ceiling: the woman manager

Marilyn J. Davidson and Cary L. Cooper, Paul Chapman Publishing, 1992

Although published in 1992, this still provides an insight into lots of the ongoing problems such as achieving visibility, relationships at work, networking, the difficulty of balancing work and home, and the problem of stress and ways of dealing with it.

The Report of the Hansard Society Commission on Women at the Top

The Hansard Society for Parliamentary Government, January 1990

A review of the position of women with regard to the glass ceiling within the different sectors of the economy.

Women at the Top. Progress after five years

Susan McRae, The Hansard Society for Parliamentary Government, March 1996. King-Hall Paper No 2

An interim, follow-up report to *The Report of The Hansard Society Commission on Women at the Top*.

Risk-taking

Feel the Fear and Do It Anyway

Susan Jeffers, Rider, 1991

Nothing to do with science and technology, but a fascinating and enjoyable read about risk-taking.

2

Almonds into peaches: education, training and lifelong learning

'Training is everything. The peach was once a bitter almond; cauliflower is nothing but cabbage with a college education.' Mark Twain

Once upon a time you started school about the age of five, left at 16 or 18, perhaps went to university and did a degree or two, and then started working. Most of your 'formal education' was crammed into the first part of your life, apart from the odd company training course or evening class. And if you missed your chance, that was it.

Education and training – like most other things in modern life – have changed, are still changing and will continue to change. Perhaps one of the most significant developments is the concept of lifelong learning: the idea that we will need to keep on learning and training, throughout our lives. Now the name of the game is 'learning happily ever after' or CPD or Continuing Professional Development – which involves 'reskilling' or 'upskilling' on a regular basis.

In response to the needs of industry and society, education and training have evolved dramatically in recent years. The following are just some of the initiatives that have put educational and training opportunities within the reach of greater numbers of adults of all ages:

- innovative vocational qualifications such as GNVQs (General National Vocational Qualifications), NVQs (National Vocational Qualifications) and Modern Apprenticeships
- Access courses to help people to acquire study skills
- part-time qualifications
- modular – 'pick and mix' type – courses which have built-in flexibility with regard to the time taken to study and the subjects studied (you might choose chemistry, Japanese, and environmental studies for example)
- distance learning – where you can study 'at a distance' (usually in your own home) using video, audio and written materials
- open learning – a flexible system of access to further training and educational resources
- CATS (Credit Accumulation and Transfer Scheme) – where you can choose single units of study, sometimes by doing courses at different institutions, or by studying part-time or at summer schools, and earn credits for specific qualifications one by one
- acceptance of ever-increasing numbers of mature students
- the proposed University for Industry.

Lifelong learning means not only that you can get a second – or third – chance, but that you can direct your own career and change direction when appropriate by building your own training portfolio, focusing on the judicious acquisition of further knowledge, skills and qualifications. Effectively used, CPD enables you to keep abreast of technical and non-technical developments and maximise your career potential.

> 'Women need:
> - *training throughout life to prepare for promotion and higher earnings; to develop modern skills; to retain and build self confidence ...*
> - *training compatible with family responsibilities, which offers provision of childcare and eldercare and courses at appropriate times and places.'*
> Women's National Commission (WNC), Women in the 90s, 1994, page 12

Qualifications can give you credibility and confidence, and although qualifications alone will not ensure that you get the job or the promotion you need, they will be a tool with which you can overcome inaccurate perceptions of your abilities. In the past statistics have demonstrated that, in general, women receive less formal training than men, and this means they can be seen as less well equipped when it comes to promotion opportunities. Fortunately, this no longer has to be the case, although you will probably discover that you will be expected to take responsibility for managing your own training and educational needs. In this context, you may find a mentor (see Chapter 4) will help you to analyse what you need to do next.

Your educational and training needs will depend on where you are now. However, whether you are a technician wondering about increasing your earning power by embarking on a part-time degree course, a graduate scientist aiming to make yourself more employable in industry, a parent returning after a career break or a senior engineer who needs to know about training for yourself or your team, the information in this chapter will provide you with an insight into the opportunities available and signposts to sources of further information.

There are two main points that are worth bearing in mind when you are considering your training needs in order to enhance your employment options.

- The first is obvious: you need to plan ahead and work out not only what you need now, but also what will be necessary by the time you've completed the training. Everything is in a state of flux, and you will need to invest in yourself to ensure that your skills are kept up to date.

- The second is that while formal qualifications are a requirement of many jobs, they are not enough in their own right. Personal transferable skills, experience and competences are of equal importance.

Personal transferable skills and competences

If you are hesitant about the value of personal transferable skills and competences, a swift trawl through the job advertisements in a single issue of the *New Scientist* will convince you of their importance and marketability, whatever your other qualifications. Consider the following extracts:

'**[organic chemist]** who must be able to organise effectively and work as part of a multi-disciplinary team ... **[mass spectrometrist]** a broad range of personal skills will be required to meet the challenges of the position and you should be industrious, highly self-motivated and an innovative problem-solver. Above all, you will have the communication and interpersonal skills to work effectively in our multi-disciplinary environment ... **[analytical chemist]** highly organised and able to work freely in multi-disciplinary teams, the ability and desire to help others and pass on skills will be essential ... **[integrated pollution inspector]** Whilst Corporate Membership of, or Chartered status within, a relevant professional body would be a distinct advantage, it will be your ability to quickly gain a thorough understanding of complex issues and your excellent communication, influencing and motivating skills that really set you apart.'

The requirement for transferable skills in the *New Scientist* adverts goes on and on:

'good **communication and reporting** skills ... will best suit candidates who thrive in a **team** environment ... ability to **work under pressure**, to tight deadlines whilst remaining focused and calm ... **languages** are a definite advantage ... excellent **strategic thinking and good planning** skills ... **decision-making** skills ... excellent organisational skills and confidence in **interpreting, integrating and summarising** data in a clear and concise way, to strict deadlines ... demonstrate a practical approach to **problem-solving** ... the ability to **influence and motivate** people at all levels ... **present complicated information** in a clear and convincing manner.'

The message is clear and unequivocal: transferable skills such as those listed above (but especially teamworking, communication, presentation and interpersonal skills), and skills which technical and scientific jobs tend to take for granted (such as numeracy, literacy, IT experience and project management) are not just desirable: they are essential.

Happily, an education and career in SET will equip you with many of these skills, and you will be able to acquire others through training – perhaps a course in public speaking to assist your presentation skills or language and cultural classes to enable you to work globally? In addition, the activities you are involved in outside work, such as service in public life or raising a family, will also equip you with transferable skills. Some of these can be accredited under Accreditation of Prior Learning schemes (APL). At the very least, they should be cited in any applications you make for courses or jobs. (The suggestions made on page 128 will help you to identify the transferable skills you will probably have developed during a career break.)

Transferable skills are something that you will want to be aware of throughout your career and which you will want to update and strengthen as and when necessary.

Formal qualifications

Courses on offer change from year to year as educational institutions strive to become more responsive to the needs of the marketplace and of their clients. When researching education and training, the obvious starting point in England and Wales could be your nearest local TEC (Training and Enterprise Council) or in Scotland LEC (Local Enterprise Company), or in Northern Ireland T&EA (Training & Employment Agency) or institute of further or higher education, but with distance and open learning now firmly established, don't limit your options without exploring further afield. (See page 132 for information on the Open University, for example.)

Naturally before embarking on any programme of learning, you will need to analyse what's right for you. The action plan on page 24 can help you to start this process.

The following pages describe some areas which you might wish to investigate further, either for yourself, your staff, or your students.

Continual changes are taking place in most areas of education and training, and although the following information is correct at the time of printing, you can keep up to date with the latest developments by contacting the individual institutions concerned, or the organisations listed.

Vocational qualifications

Vocational qualifications such as ONCs (Ordinary National Certificates), ONDs (Ordinary National Diplomas), HNCs (Higher National Certificates) and HNDs (Higher National Diplomas) have been around for some time and have earned the respect of employers. Many people have studied for these qualifications both as a skills and knowledge base in their own right, and as a stepping stone to a degree.

Action Plan: What do you need to know next?

First work out what you're aiming for.

❑ Draw up a list of your strengths under the headings of 'Knowledge areas' and 'Transferable skills'. (The transferable skills requested in the *New Scientist* adverts may be a useful starting point.)

❑ Draw up a list of your 'development areas' (weaknesses!) under the same headings. (If you did a SWOT analysis after reading Chapter 1, this might be useful here.)

❑ At this stage, are you looking to enhance your strengths or develop skills and expertise in areas which otherwise might hold you back?
Many people find it is effective to concentrate on technical skills in the early years and supervisory and management skills in the later ones.

❑ Do you have a particular job or promotion in mind?
If so, list the areas you might need to work on to fulfil the requirements of that position.

❑ List the specific benefits that you would hope to achieve from doing further training.

❑ If your employer is supporting you, what might they be seeking to achieve from your training?

Now concentrate on analysing the training opportunities which could meet your needs. Don't limit yourself to courses: consider other opportunities such as on-the-job training, secondments, specific projects, distance learning and computer training packages, all of which might have a valid role to play in your lifelong learning.

❑ Which training opportunities could be available to you now?

❑ Of these, which best fulfil your requirements?

❑ And of these, which meet your practical limitations: cost? time? location? any other limitations?

(If you have family responsibilities, you might also wish to consider the list on page 131.)

Try to talk to some people who have recently completed the course or development activity you are considering, and get their impressions.

Find out about how to apply for such opportunities, and particularly whether there are any application deadlines involved and what you need to do next.

Once you have embarked upon further training, it is useful to review how far it is meeting your original aims, and analyse what you would do differently in the future.

Julie Ashton, quality compliance manager

Julie Ashton is a good example of someone who has advanced her career by studying for further educational, vocational and professional qualifications part-time. She left school at 16, went to a local college for a year and then joined Roche Products as a quality control analyst. She is now in her early 30s.

I didn't like school, and I especially didn't like the new secondary school I attended when we moved to the Southeast from the North. So it wasn't surprising that when I left school at 16 I was a bit of a rebel. Careers guidance at the school was useless and I wasn't really focused: my social life was more important to me than my career! My best subjects at school had been biology and chemistry and so I applied to do a one-year City & Guilds course in Laboratory Technology at the local college. Then I joined Roche as a quality control analyst where my work involved the routine testing of drugs.

It was hard to get used to the discipline of working but I soon realised that if I wanted to get on, I needed an education, so when the company offered me the opportunity to do a day-release TEC 3 in Chemistry [equivalent to an ONC], I thought, yes, why not? It took me two years to get the qualification and another two to get to TEC 5 level [equivalent to an HNC]. I can't say I enjoyed it: the studying was tedious, but I did get a buzz out of passing exams. I get bored if I don't have a new challenge every six months or so, and by the time I'd gained the final qualification I was very bored with a straightforward analyst's role, even though I was regularly given increasing responsibility. I compensated by having a wild social life and got to know most of the London clubs!

The certificates I had so far been awarded satisfied the entry requirements for a degree course and so I decided to do a part-time BSc in Applied Chemistry at what was then Hatfield Polytechnic and is now the University of Hertfordshire. That took one day a week for four years. The degree was modular so you could choose different options and I discovered that I was very interested in medicinal chemistry, physiology and pharmacology – and that, ironically, I didn't excel at analytical chemistry! I knew then that I didn't want to stay in the laboratory but expand into other areas.

Whilst I was studying for my degree I progressed up the career ladder from analyst, to research analyst, and then to senior research analyst, where I was developing methods of analysis for new drugs. Once I had a degree, my status automatically changed – I was now a qualified chemist. Soon after I was looking ahead again and started networking. This enabled me to make the big jump to a quality assurance officer within the production environment. This job was very different as it involved supervisory responsibility: I had to supervise seven people responsible for the sampling of raw materials, testing of components and sampling of products, and I also had to monitor manufacturing standards. During this period I was promoted to production compliance section head.

In my own time I was still studying, this time on a two-year distance learning course for a Postgraduate Diploma in Pharmaceutical Studies. That was hard: it was a lot of work. I passed, and then went on to apply for Qualified Person registration. It's very tough achieving this status as it requires a lot of dedication and experience. The company has to sponsor you and, because it's a very expensive procedure, you have to be good. Being a Qualified Person means that you have expert knowledge and are one of the few people legally allowed to release pharmaceutical products (drugs) onto the market. Once qualified, your name is entered into a legal register and onto your company's manufacturing licence. It's a huge responsibility and at first that's rather daunting, but you have the confidence of knowing you are well trained with a great deal of expert knowledge.

The assessment procedure for registration culminates in an interview with a board of examiners including representatives from the Royal Society of Chemistry, the Institute of Biology and the Royal Pharmaceutical Society of Great Britain. The interview was a success and when I walked out of that interview room, I knew that my career in pharmaceuticals could now really take off.

As well as formal qualifications, I've also been on a lot of different courses organised by Roche to develop management and other skills such as problem-solving, negotiation, leadership and team-motivation. I've also learned from other people. As a 25 year old, I had to manage seven older men, all highly experienced in their fields. I was nervous about that, but after a few hiccups, they taught me a lot. My management style has changed a lot since then: I used to be quite aggressive, but now I empathise more.

Would I recommend learning and working? You need to think very carefully about it: you need to be very dedicated and disciplined as you're on your own and not in a learning environment. But I'm glad I did it this way: you do learn a lot quicker and I think you mature faster. And you're also earning *and* gaining experience.

Since achieving Qualified Person registration, my career is still developing. I've continued my progression up the career ladder and increased my responsibilities: I manage three teams of people, and I'm responsible for many quality assurance activities including the releasing and distribution of Roche products in the UK. I report directly to the quality director. My job is ever changing and evolving.

My latest challenge has been adding the management of the Microbiology Laboratory. From a junior analyst to managing a large part of a multinational's quality assurance department – not bad for someone who left full-time education at 17. But I don't intend to stop here.

Added importance and impetus have been given to vocational qualifications by governmental and employer initiatives to develop and promote the NVQ and GNVQ range of qualifications.

NVQs

NVQs are entirely work-based and do not require any prior qualifications. They are specific to a particular occupation, although they also encompass transferable skills. They are designed to show that you are competent in a certain skill at a certain level in a certain job. There are different NVQ levels available, ranging from Level 1, which provides evidence of routine skills, to Level 5, which demonstrates complex managerial and professional abilities. Modern Apprenticeships (see page 29) aim to achieve at least an NVQ Level 3, which is equivalent to two A-levels. The underpinning knowledge required for the successful completion on an NVQ may be gained in a variety of ways which *can* include academic courses.

The Qualifications Curriculum Authority (QCA) can give details of the many awarding bodies for NVQs. This is a new authority and at the time of writing, the temporary contact details for this organisation are:

QCA
Customer Services
222 Euston Road
London
NW1 2BZ
Tel: 0171 728 1914; fax: 0171 916 5799

GNVQs

GNVQs are school or college-based and cover the knowledge and skills relating to a broad range of careers within a specific employment sector. They are usually full-time courses which may have an element of work placement. GNVQs are currently available at several levels of difficulty including Foundation, Intermediate and Advanced. An Advanced GNVQ is equivalent to two A-levels. It is possible that some GNVQ courses can provide the underpinning knowledge for NVQs at lower levels. GNVQs are also used to gain access to higher education courses.

There are three awarding bodies for SET GNVQs; contact their customer enquiries units for detailed information on their individual courses or optional modules, and their other vocational qualifications.

Edexcel Foundation (formerly Business & Technology Education Council - BTEC)
Stewart House
32 Russell Square
London
WC1B 5DN
Tel: 0171 393 4444; fax: 0171 393 4445

City & Guilds
1 Giltspur Street
London
EC1A 9DD
Tel: 0171 294 2468; fax: 0171 294 2400

RSA (Royal Society of Arts) Examinations Board
Westwood Way
Coventry
CV4 8HS
Tel: 01203 470 033; fax: 01203 468 080

The following table gives you a rough idea of how the different qualifications 'line up', but it is not intended to be definitive.

How the various qualifications compare		
Work-based qualifications	**Vocational qualifications**	**Academic qualifications**
NVQ Level 5	Some postgraduate degrees Professional qualifications	Some postgraduate degrees
NVQ Level 4	Degree	Degree
NVQ Level 3	Advanced GNVQ	(2) A-levels (4) AS-levels
NVQ Level 2	Intermediate GNVQ	(4 or 5) GCSEs (grades A*–C)
NVQ Level 1	Foundation GNVQ	(4 or 5) GCSEs (grades D–G)

(A Part One GNVQ is half the content of a full GNVQ and can be taken at Foundation or Intermediate Level; it is equivalent to 2 GCSEs at the appropriate grades.)

The Scottish Vocational Qualifications (SVQs) are equivalent to their English counterparts.

Many NVQ and GNVQ programmes focus on specific areas of SET but *all* NVQs and GNVQs place great emphasis on key skills such as oral and written communications, numeracy and IT. As these vocational qualifications gain ground, they are likely to have a profound effect on careers within SET, some people even arguing: 'The reason NVQs pose a challenge to professional engineers, as to other professions, is that employers can now legally use non-professionally trained staff to do tasks traditionally reserved for those with professional qualifications, provided competence can be shown.' Julia Evetts, *Gender and Career in Science and Engineering*, 1996, page 35

The ECCTIS+ (Education Counselling and Credit Transfer Information Service) database includes information on certain non-degree courses – see page 31.

Modern Apprenticeships

Modern Apprenticeships were introduced in the UK in 1995 and are backed by the Government and employers, and in many cases (particularly in engineering manufacturing) they have been developed with employers, or by employer-led partnerships between Industry Training Organisations and TECs/LECs and the Department for Education and Employment (DfEE). Modern Apprenticeships aim to offer young people a means of earning and learning by providing a route for gaining respected qualifications (at least an NVQ Level 3), key skills and relevant work experience. In some cases further education qualifications are also either mandatory (engineering manufacture) or suggested.

Modern Apprenticeships are highly relevant to careers in SET, and many employers have now embarked on successful schemes. Like other vocational qualifications, Modern Apprenticeships have earned acceptance as a valid route into higher education.

At the time of writing, the upper age limit for funding available for Modern Apprenticeships is 25, but various organisations are lobbying for this to be removed, and for Modern Apprenticeships to be made available for people of any age who wish to reskill or change direction.

Your local careers service or TEC/LEC should be able to supply you with details of the Modern Apprenticeship opportunities that are available locally; or you can get a free information pack by telephoning 0345 66 55 88. For more general information contact:

Department for Education and Employment (DfEE)
Training for Young People Division
Room W4D
Moorfoot
Sheffield S1 4PQ
Tel: 0114 259 3573; fax: 0114 259 3565;
website: http://www.open.gov.uk/dfee/maprintro.htm

First degrees

The combinations of subjects, the educational institutions, and the varying approaches to doing a first degree have mushroomed in recent years, and so the aim of this section is to signpost some of the issues you might want to think about and highlight sources of further information.

With so much on offer, it can be hard to keep an open mind without drowning in choice. Ask yourself:

- Are you limited by geographical location? Have you thought about distance learning?
- Do you want to do the degree full-time or part-time?
- Would you prefer a more vocational or more academic style of course?
- Would a modular course or a CATS scheme (see page 20) be more suitable for you?
- Do you want to do a straight degree or have you thought about combining it with something else – business or languages for example?
- What benefits might you get from doing a sandwich degree?
- If you have worked or trained previously in a relevant area, will you be able to gain credits for APL?

Checklist: Choosing your course

You will want to develop your own checklist of criteria which you will apply to each institution you are considering, but you might like to find out about the following:

- ❑ cost – including 'hidden extras' such as special equipment or clothing, or professional examination fees
- ❑ course structure, teaching methods, size of teaching groups and so on
- ❑ the opportunity to study or work abroad
- ❑ male:female ratios on the course – what is the implication here? would it influence your choice of course?
- ❑ nature and quality of any work experience placements
- ❑ the teaching of transferable skills
- ❑ the university's teaching and research ratings
- ❑ employment statistics and destinations of graduates of the course you are considering
- ❑ learning 'outcomes' – another buzzword which means does the degree course specify what you will have achieved in terms of knowledge, cognitive and practical skills, and understanding once you have finished your course?

There are many excellent sources of information available comparing different universities and degree courses – see the Further Reading section on page 49 or you could investigate ECCTIS.

ECCTIS+

ECCTIS+ is the UK's national computer database for further and higher education opportunities. Regularly updated, it holds details on over 100,000 courses at more than a thousand universities and colleges of further and higher education. It can help you to identify the universities and colleges that run courses that interest you. ECCTIS is available in most schools and colleges, careers services, TECs/LECs, TAPs (Training Access Points – see page 39) and on the Internet at http://www.ecctis.co.uk. Alternatively, contact:

ECCTIS 2000 Ltd
Oriel House
Oriel Road
Cheltenham GL50 1XP
Tel: 01242 252 627; fax: 01242 258 600

Higher degrees

There is a confusingly wide range of postgraduate degrees available, but by this stage you should be in a position to judge what suits you best, whether that is an MSc or a PhD, full-time or part-time, and at which institution. Once again, some sources of further information are provided here. Perhaps the main message is to take time to mull over all your options – there is now much more choice than there used to be. Masters' degrees, for example, can mean different things at different institutions: it could be a short conversion course, a taught degree course, or a shorter research degree, so you will need to find out precisely what's involved. There are also many 'new subjects' on offer, and highly specialised courses have been developed, such as the course in the following advertisement.

MSc in Science Communication
(Full or part-time)

Communicating science is a growth industry with an abundance of career opportunities in publishing, writing, museum and exhibition work, marketing, public relations and television, radio and multimedia production.

This course helps science and engineering graduates develop the necessary analytical and practical skills for work in these areas. Throughout the course, students are encouraged to develop their creative abilities to communicate science, technology and medicine in fresh and more effective ways.

Imperial College of Science, Technology and Medicine
London SW7 2AZ
Tel: 0171 594 8753 Fax: 0171 594 8763

You might also want to consider doing a higher degree in another country. This can increase your marketability as you will probably acquire both international experience (and networks), and some language skills. If you don't speak another language fluently yet, don't let this put you off. Many universities abroad, for example the internationally recognised Chalmers University of Technology in Sweden, run higher degree courses taught entirely in English.

If you are choosing a research topic, you might find it useful to draw up a simple action plan to assist your decision-making.

Action Plan: Researching your topic

❑ Identify your potential topics.
❑ What are the benefits and risks of each potential topic?
❑ Once you are considering a particular topic, ask yourself whether you will be able to keep it sharply focused and well defined?
❑ Is there a strong chance of a useful outcome?
❑ Having decided on a topic, choose your advisors with care. They can make a vital difference to the success of your research. Madhu Bhabuta (see page 47) offers some advice on this subject.
❑ As your research proceeds, monitor your progress at intervals. Are you still targeted?
❑ If the likelihood of success is becoming doubtful, review how you can alter your direction.

Part-time degrees

You may find that the company or organisation you work for is willing to assist you to do a part-time degree. Although most part-time students are mature (over 21), an increasing number of younger people, like Julie Ashton (see page 25), are also opting for this style of learning as it can combine earning with gaining a qualification in a cost-effective and career-effective way. Sometimes you can switch from a part-time degree to a full-time degree and vice versa.

Many institutions now run part-time courses for undergraduate and postgraduate degrees and other qualifications. One of the best known is Birkbeck College at the University of London.

Birkbeck College

'Birkbeck and the other member colleges of the University of London have many research interests in common and share the same standards and degree structures, but in one important respect Birkbeck is unique. Our distinctive characteristic is our provision for the mature, part-time student. At postgraduate level, in particular, we have developed a lively academic community, allowing mature part-time students to study alongside the more conventional full-time students.

We are very conscious of our origin as a Mechanics' Institution, advocating self-help through self-improvement, and much of our formal teaching still takes place in the evening for the benefit of our part-time students. We are particularly proud to maintain an undergraduate programme that is wholly part-time, giving the widest possible access to higher education for working people.' *Birkbeck Postgraduate Prospectus*, 1996–97, page 4

For more information contact:

Birkbeck College
University of London
Malet Street
London
WC1E 7HX
Tel: 0171 631 6000; fax: 0171 631 6270

Your nearest university might also run part-time or distance learning courses, and of course you could study through the Open University (OU) wherever you live. (There is a feature on the OU on page 132.)

Winning Women

Winning Women is a research project being conducted at the Universities of Stirling and Dundee and funded by the Scottish Higher Education Funding Council (SHEFC). Its aim is to study ways of encouraging women to study science, engineering and technology subjects in higher education. The project, which comprises the first and third phase of SHEFC's Women into Science, Engineering and Technology initiative, is researching into ways of improving women's chances of succeeding in SET. Three interlinked guides to good practice in access, participation and progression in SET, which individuals and organisations can use to change current practice, are to be published in Autumn 1997. The guides will be available in conventional and electronic format. For further information and publication details, contact:

Winning Women Project
Maureen Cooper
Department of Chemistry
University of Stirling
Stirling
FK9 4LA
Tel: 01786 467 781;
website: http://www.dundee.ac.uk/design/winning.html;
email: m.e.cooper@stir.ac.uk

Management qualifications

At some stage in your career, the development of your job might start to demand more management skills or you may decide you want to move out of straight SET and into a more managerial role. If so, you could consider studying for a management qualification which would help ensure that you have the skills necessary for such a transition.

An MBA (Master of Business Administration) is probably the best-known postgraduate qualification in this context and is designed to equip you for a senior management position. You will need to have several years' work experience if you are to gain the most benefit from embarking on an MBA programme, and indeed the best courses stipulate this. This could coincide with the time you are also thinking about starting a family, which is perhaps one reason why there tends to be a low percentage of women on MBA courses.

There are many institutions now offering MBAs, and like any other course, these can be of varying quality and content (although most cover management, human resources, finance and accounting). As always, you will need to work out what your needs are and choose a course accordingly: identify what you are aiming to achieve by doing an MBA, and try to ensure that the course will satisfy both those objectives and the needs of any future employer. In particular, an MBA could be a qualification that would be worth studying for abroad, so that you could add a new language to your transferable skills and an international dimension to your skills portfolio.

Michele Mooney's profile demonstrates how an MBA helped her to achieve a career move.

Michele Mooney, card services business development manager

Michele Mooney is in her early 40s. She began her career teaching geology in a school. Now she is using leading edge technology to develop new business areas for British Telecommunications.

I enjoyed teaching geology but after eight years I realised that I could either aim for a headship or move into the business world. Unfortunately, although I had the transferable skills to make this latter move, I wasn't *perceived* as having them. I talked to someone who had done an MBA and realised that such a broad-based course could offer me the official 'recognition' that I was lacking, as well as insights, additional skills and new knowledge. An MBA could be a passport to a promotion within education or out into industry.

The MBA course was totally fascinating, stimulating and exhausting. I was exposed to a whole new world of subjects and ideas and I was meeting a large group of interesting people from a variety of backgrounds and experiences. My scientific background came in useful, providing as it did a sound base of numeracy (particularly useful in the accountancy, economics and statistics courses), and the ability to absorb vast amounts of information whilst still paying attention to the details. I tend to think in terms of models and pictures in a shorthand way, and this proved invaluable with so much to cram into such a short space of time. My years spent teaching meant I was used to ploughing through quantities of work at unsocial hours!

For much of the course we worked in different study groups; this was intended to increase our teamworking skills, and we soon appreciated that to succeed you needed a good team. The good teams were brilliant; the bad ones were disastrous.

The qualifications, skills (including a new language) and experience I gained from the MBA course gave me a better idea of where I wanted to go, and enabled me to apply for jobs in industry and eventually get a position in telecommunications.

Over the last decade I've worked in various areas: I've been a strategic analyst for Yellow Pages, launched a messaging service and developed a personal communications programme. My present position developing new products has meant my return to the very leading edge of technology and I love the fact that I'm solving problems that haven't been solved before. My current project is developing a multi-application smart card which will have personal ID and digital signature capability. This has enormous implications for society, as once people can perform transactions securely and confidentially by email and Internet, electronic commerce will take off.

Ironically, even in this area I find that my geological background has been very important. Geology involves making connections across a wide range of disciplines, and my work involves spotting potential links and themes across different technologies. The fact that I'm not an expert is an advantage: what is important, is that I know how to ask the right questions. I think women have the edge here: they often have a different map in their head and they can get away with asking questions which may seem simple, but which can be very revealing.

For me the MBA was great as it taught me to understand business in a more rigorous way, equipped me with greater flexibility and acknowledged skills, and gave me a palette of techniques which allowed me to 'paint' myself a new career.

The Association of MBAs (AMBA) can provide you with further information on MBA courses, or consult the books on page 49.

AMBA
15 Duncan Terrace
London
N1 8BZ
Tel: 0171 837 3375; fax: 0171 278 3634

Company training

Although as a new recruit you might be introduced to the organisational culture through an induction course, very few companies now provide a highly structured, across-the-board training programme. Today most organisations seek to employ people from a wide range of backgrounds with a healthy mix of skills, and by implication this usually means individual training plans – or to put it more bluntly, 'ask-for-it-and-organise-it-yourself' training programmes.

Other companies develop their own tailor-made courses in specific areas, and at different stages in your career you may be expected to acquire new skills and knowledge which will enable you to do your job more effectively. At times, you might be a little daunted by the demands that can be made of you – for instance, a short course where you are expected to get to grips with a complex new technology – but you will find that your career in general will benefit if you can embrace the opportunities that you are offered.

Within organisations, training opportunities do not always appear in the guise of formal courses, although your company may support you if you wish to work towards any of the qualifications listed in the first part of this chapter. On-the-job training, secondments to another division, or working on a specific project, reading books and journals, attending conferences, or learning a language, are all ways in which you can increase your skills portfolio.

A good employer will support you in your training aims, but the nature of the relationship is more likely to be that of a 'partnership', and it will usually be up to you to make sure you get the input you need. It usually helps to write yourself an action plan, and review and revise it at regular intervals (see page 24).

While it might not be the best idea to interrogate potential employers too brutally about the training offered in a preliminary interview, it is worth discovering from their letterhead whether they are 'Investors in People'. This is a national standard designed to encourage employers to improve their training and development (and consequently their business performance and competitiveness) by helping their staff to identify and fulfil their training needs. If the organisation you are considering does not have an 'Investors in People' logo on its letterhead, you might want to find out whether they are seeking accreditation.

Once you have secured a position within the company, try to take full advantage of any appraisal or mentoring schemes (see Chapter 4) to identify your development areas and to initiate ways of strengthening them.

'In our business nothing stands still and if our people don't develop, the world will develop around them and they will be left behind. We are looking for rounded individuals with transferable skills so our training policy covers both professional and personal development. We have an extensive range of training programmes. These cover basic skills training in such areas as report writing, presentation delivery, supervisory, influencing and negotiation. We also offer personal development workshops and professional further education such as advanced seminar programmes and university affiliated courses. Staff are encouraged to use our extensive library and on-line research facilities.

The whole ethos of our company is to encourage and enable our people to continuously develop so that they – and the organisation – don't stagnate.' Senior personnel adviser in a large global healthcare company

Professional qualifications

As you start to become established in a career, you will probably need to acquire professional recognition, often by joining a learned or professional society or institution. The names and contact details of some of the most well-known institutions are included in the list of Useful Addresses on page 207 onwards. Make sure that the institution you are joining will provide you with CPD opportunities (see box).

CPD and your professional institution

As mentioned earlier, you can expect to engage in CPD (Continuing Professional Development) throughout your working life, whether through reading, attending conferences, or formal study. Accordingly most professional institutions now expect you to engage in a certain amount of updating and learning each year in order to ensure that your skills and knowledge are still current.

The literature of the Institution of Electronics and Electrical Incorporated Engineers (IEEIE) demonstrates some of the types of training you might want your professional society to offer.

'Continuing Professional Development

The Institution strongly supports members in honouring their commitment to Continuing Professional Development (CPD).

An IEEIE Record of Professional Development is available providing a structured approach to CPD planning and a practical and convenient means of recording achievements.

A full and regular programme of National, Regional and Professional Group Lectures is arranged and there are occasional Symposia and Conferences on topical themes and newly emerging technologies.

The IEEIE stages a successful nationwide programme of short courses. Topics cover a broad spectrum of technical and non-technical areas of professional relevance to members including: Electrical Installation; Electromagnetic Compatibility; Control, Communications and Data; Technical Management; Health and Safety; Personal Effectiveness.

The Institution has developed a number of successful open learning courses which benefit from the active involvement by members as tutors. Topics include: Mathematics; Wiring Regulations (16th Edition); A Practical Guide to Tackling the Job Market.' *IEEIE information pack*, 1997

Other sources of information

There are various sources of information on education and training which should be available locally.

Careers services

Each region has a local careers guidance service which, since they have become independent of the Government and each other, vary in name, in scope and in 'target audiences'. Most should be able to provide you with detailed information on opportunities in the region, although you may have to pay for this advice. You can find out the name and address of your local service through your local library or citizens' advice bureau.

If you are a graduate, find out whether you can use your university careers service on a lifelong basis.

TECs, LECs and T&EAs

TECs in England and Wales, LECs in Scotland and T&EAs in Northern Ireland – promoted as 'gateways to learning' – may be able to provide access to a range of assistance and information about personal and business development opportunities, including returning to work or training courses, and sometimes about childcare support for people re-entering education. The address of your nearest TEC, LEC or T&EA should be in your telephone book.

SET organisations

The Engineering and Marine Training Authority (EMTA), the national training organisation for engineering, and EEF (Engineering Employers' Federation) regional offices will also be able to provide you with further specific information. Relevant addresses can be found on page 208.

TAPs

These databases of training courses are aimed primarily at careers advisers but you might be able to gain access to the information via your local library, jobcentre, or TEC/LEC office. TAPs provide a wide range of information on full-time, part-time and short courses in further, higher and adult education, courses run by TECs and LECs, and private courses run by independent and commercial training companies.

Jobcentres

Don't overlook your local jobcentre. It can be worth checking out what's on offer, especially if you are trying to get back into work, or into work for the first time. At the very least, staff at the jobcentre should be able to point you in other directions.

Building your own training portfolio

You can easily build your own training portfolio which can comprise different versions of your CV (curriculum vitae - see page 55) and an action plan. The action plan on page 24 and the one below may help you to develop your own ideas.

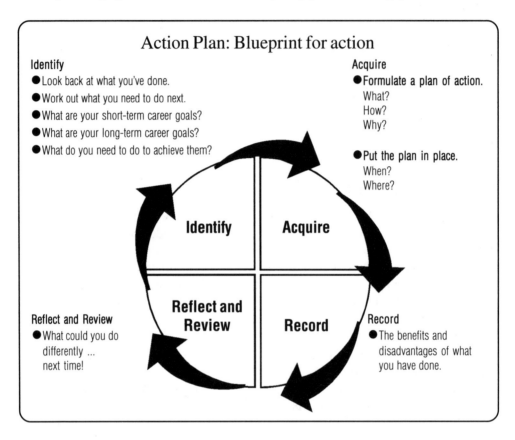

Action Plan: Blueprint for action

Identify
- Look back at what you've done.
- Work out what you need to do next.
- What are your short-term career goals?
- What are your long-term career goals?
- What do you need to do to achieve them?

Acquire
- Formulate a plan of action.
  What?
  How?
  Why?

- Put the plan in place.
  When?
  Where?

Reflect and Review
- What could you do differently ... next time!

Record
- The benefits and disadvantages of what you have done.

Records of Achievement

There are various national and European initiatives which are intended to offer individuals a formal means of continuously monitoring and recording achievements and analysing and recording progress, sometimes with specific relevance to particular sectors of business and industry. These include:

- UK Government initiatives such as the new National Record of Achievement – the proposed ProFile

- and a European-wide professional record of achievement in engineering, known as the EuroRecord (see page 41).

Most of these initiatives are still in the early stages of testing and development. However the general intention with most of these documents is that they are designed to be used either privately or publicly, as tools to record achievements and as a means of promoting constructive reflection, and thereby assist in lifelong learning and career planning.

The EuroRecord

The European Professional Record of Achievement in Engineering – the EuroRecord – is a pilot project under the EU LEONARDO Programme. It aims to provide a common language and common structure for recording CPD by helping engineers and other professionals within the European engineering industry to:

- 'draw up and document competence development plans and the resulting requirements for learning and for personal and professional development
- record learning achievements and professional development, wherever, and however, it occurs, and accumulate credit towards relevant qualifications linked to the learning plan.'

Find out more by telephoning the project manager on 01223 332 722 (fax: 01223 301 122; email: ah223@cam.ac.uk)

Checklist: A personal record

If you are not eligible for any of the schemes mentioned above, you can draw up your own 'career and competence development' plan. If you complete this in some detail, it will provide a useful database which should enable you to:

❏ determine whether you can seek Accreditation of Prior Learning (APL) for previous learning and experience, whether this is formal or work-based
❏ demonstrate that you meet the requirements of a professional body for membership, fellowship, chartered status or similar
❏ use it as a database from which to develop your various CVs, emphasising your achievements, strengths and transferable skills and competences
❏ use it as the basis of a job or promotion application
❏ identify your development areas, and subsequently develop your own CPD plan.

Investing in your future

Like many women, you may find it hard to justify spending money on yourself, and be worried about the consequences of a reduction in income that further education or training might involve. Remember, it is not only desirable – it will probably be *essential* – to invest in yourself if you are to sustain a successful career.

If you have decided to do a degree or further training, there are a number of sources of finance that you can investigate. Obviously what you are eligible for and how much you can get will depend on your individual circumstances, but the following checklist offers some guidance.

Grants, loans, tuition fees and other sources of funding are under constant review and are being altered as the result of Government policy and other factors. The following checklist was accurate at the time of writing, but contact the bodies concerned for current information. The criteria for eligibility, conditions and what's on offer are changing, in view of the conclusions of the 1997 report by the National Committee of Inquiry into Higher Education – *Higher Education in the Learning Society* – chaired by Sir Ron Dearing. Mandatory awards and tuition fees are particularly affected.

Checklist: Financing your career training

Mandatory awards
What's on offer?
At the time of writing mandatory awards are made up of tuition fees and means-tested grants for maintenance. Tuition fees are paid straight to your university, whereas grants will be paid to you individually every term. In normal circumstances, you will not have to pay back your mandatory awards.

The amount of grant you receive will depend on whether you are living at home or away and where you're studying. It is means-tested so it takes into account how much your parents (or husband or wife) earn.

Are you eligible?
- ❑ Have you been living in Britain for three years prior to starting your course?
- ❑ Are you doing an appropriate course? (Check with the booklets listed on page 43.)
- ❑ Will this be the first time you have received money from public funds to be on a higher education course?

If you can answer 'yes' to all the above questions, you could be eligible for a mandatory award.

For further information
You can obtain further information from your Local Education Authority (LEA), or the Department for Education and Employment (DfEE) on 0171 510 0150 – ask for the latest booklet/information on *Student Grants and Loans*. In Scotland the Student Awards Agency (tel: 0131 244 5823) publishes *Student Grants in Scotland*, and in Ireland the Department of Education for Northern Ireland (tel: 01247 279279) publishes *Grants and Loans to Students*. You will then need to contact your LEA – or the Student Awards Agency in Scotland or the Education and Library Boards in Northern Ireland – before you start your course.

Access funds

What's on offer?
Access funds are administered by your university for the benefit of students in financial hardship. The good news is that you do not have to pay access funds back but the bad news is that there are always more people applying for them than there is money available.

Are you eligible?
- ❑ Are you currently studying on a full-time university course?
- ❑ Are you in serious financial difficulties?
- ❑ Have you already taken out the full amount of student loan available to you?

If you can answer 'yes' to all the above questions, you could be eligible for some money from your university's access fund.

For further information
Contact your students union officer, or the university welfare officer, or ask your tutor.

Student loans

What's on offer?
Student loans are administered by the Student Loans Company. The amount of the loan varies according to where you live and the year of your course, but it's not dependent on your parents' or partner's income.

After you have finished your course, you will have to pay back your loan (plus interest) within a specified period.

Are you eligible?
- ❑ Are you going to start an appropriate course before you are 50?

If so, subject to certain conditions, you should be able to take out a student loan.

For further information
Contact the Student Loans Company on Freefone 0800 40 50 10 and ask for its leaflet and/or further information on student loans, or visit its home page on http://www.slc.co.uk

Alternatively talk to your bank.

Career Development Loans

What's on offer?
A Career Development Loan (CDL) is a deferred repayment bank loan which provides you with initial help to pay for vocational education or training. CDLs are managed by the DfEE together with four 'High Street' banks – Barclays, the Co-Operative, the Clydesdale, and the Royal Bank of Scotland. After your course has finished, you will have to repay the loan plus interest.

Are you eligible?
- ❑ Will you be over 18 on the date of application?
- ❑ Are you unable to get other funding to pay for your course?
- ❑ Is your course job-related?
- ❑ Do you intend to live or train in Great Britain, and afterwards work in the EU or European Economic Area?
- ❑ Will your course involve no more than two years' study or training?

If your answer is yes to all these questions, you should be eligible for a loan. You do not already have to be a customer of one of the banks concerned.

For further information
Telephone Freefone 0800 585 505 for further information on Career Development Loans, or contact your local TEC/LEC or jobcentre, or one of the banks named.

Social security benefits

Only a few students now receive social security and housing benefits.

Are you eligible?
- ❑ Are you a lone parent?
- ❑ Do you have a disability?

If you can answer 'yes' to either of the above questions, you could be eligible for social security benefits. The number of your nearest Benefits Agency or Social Security Office will be in your local telephone directory.

Overdrafts

If you are considering a bank overdraft to finance your education or training, remember that the rate of interest on overdrafts is usually higher than that on money borrowed from places like the Student Loans Company.

Sponsorship

Several firms are willing to sponsor students. *Sponsorship for Students* (CRAC/Hobsons Publishing plc) explains the pros and cons of sponsorship, how sponsorship works and includes a guide to UK firms offering sponsorship. *Sponsorship and Training Opportunities in Engineering* (published by the Institution of Mechanical Engineers whose address is on page 209) lists employers who are keen to sponsor students. Most sponsorship schemes are aimed at younger students.

Income tax

You may be able to offset the expense of some vocational courses against your income tax liability. Check with the educational institution concerned whether the course qualifies for tax relief. It can also be worth contacting your nearest tax enquiry office (the telephone number will be in your local directory under Inland Revenue) for the most recent information. Bear in mind, though, that the application of the rules can vary from region to region, so it is worth investigating the matter thoroughly.

Scholarships, bursaries and other sources of funds

Some organisations have scholarships or bursaries available, several of them specifically directed at women. The following are amongst the best known in SET:

IEE Engineering Degree Scholarships for Women
The Institution of Electrical Engineers
Savoy Place
London
WC2R 0BL
Tel: 0171 240 1871; fax: 0171 240 7735

The Caroline Haslett Memorial Trust Scholarships
The Institution of Electronics and Electrical Incorporated Engineers
Savoy Hill House
Savoy Hill
London
WC2R 0BS
Tel: 0171 836 3357; fax: 0171 497 9006

The Lady Finniston Awards
c/o The Institution of Mechanical Incorporated Engineers
3 Birdcage Walk
Westminster
London
SW1H 9JN
Tel: 0171 799 1808; fax: 0171 799 2243

- ❑ ECCTIS (see page 31) has an in-depth section on grants and loans.
- ❑ You might want to consider training as a teacher: in recognition of the importance of having excellent SET teachers in schools, there are special funds available under the Priority Subject Recruitment Scheme for those who wish to retrain as a teacher in shortage subjects such as science and mathematics – see page 168.
- ❑ Women returners could also consider the funding sources listed on pages 133-34.
- ❑ Other research scholarships include the Dorothy Hodgkin Fellowships (see page 152) and The Wellcome Trust fellowships (see page 134).
- ❑ The addresses of the relevant Research Councils are given on pages 151-52.
- ❑ You could use the books listed on page 50 to find out whether there are any other grants administered by charities, trust funds or university scholarships which you can apply for, including EU scholarship programmes.

Madhu Bhabuta, research assistant in computing

Madhu D. K. Bhabuta is in her mid 20s. She is in the final stages of her doctoral studies at Imperial College of Science, Technology and Medicine. She is also one of the managing directors of Internet Online Ltd, a technical consultancy and web design company.

Both my parents are powerful role models for me. My father has always encouraged me to explore and discover, but it was my mother, a mathematics teacher and the deputy head of my school, who inspired me to learn mathematics and exposed me to the intellectual challenges of the subject. My interest in technology and mathematics led me to engineering and I chose to do the MEng in Software Engineering at Imperial College of Science, Technology and Medicine.

At the beginning of the course I found it hard to cope; out of the 120 or so students, only about 10% were girls, and out of the 35 students registered for the MEng, there were just two girls. My lack of confidence was a problem as I did not understand the psychology of the 'young male', but I had some very good friends who helped me get on my feet. I would warn any young women who are considering doing an engineering degree (especially if, like me, they don't have brothers), that they might find the beginning of their degree course hard, but they should persist. Believe in yourself and once you have established your position in the class or group, people will start to respect you for *who* you are, and not for *what* you are. It is also important not to be intimidated by the reputation of the college: go for the best.

Something else I find critical in a degree course is the industrial placement. During my industrial placement, I worked at the Chief Engineers' Unit, ICL, Bracknell, for six months and was lucky in that my supervisor there acted as an informal mentor. I learned to use UNIX at an expert level, to work to very real deadlines, deal with difficult people, and in particular learnt a lot of the 'technical tools' that I still use today. It was exciting to work at a high level: I was working alongside the top engineers at ICL, designing a new parallel computer. Significantly it was here that I started using the techniques that I have subsequently developed during my PhD.

After graduation I would have been happy to work in industry – I'd found my industrial placement challenging and fun. I had also recognised that research can be done in industry too, but I was offered a superb PhD place to research and analyse Asynchronous Transfer Mode (ATM) networks.

Today's networks are too slow to handle the demands of tomorrow's technological developments. ATM is the latest solution to this problem. It is designed to be flexible and very fast. My PhD involves investigating the characteristics of traffic going through networks, and developing mathematical models to understand ATM traffic and designing switches that can cope with the future needs of the Internet. Yet another part of my research concerns how we are going to charge users. After all, the only way to create large-scale interest in new technologies is to demonstrate their profitability. My work thus focuses on immensely relevant and practical problems with a strong mathematical and theoretical basis.

I have now almost finished the research and I have had an excellent supervisor who is well known in his area. Your choice of supervisor can be critical to the success of your PhD; my advice would be to choose a supervisor who is very interested in the kind of work you are intending to do and who will be responsive. If you start doing things they are not interested in, you might find yourself boxed into a corner. Make sure your potential supervisor has no inhibitions about working with women and is someone you could build a good rapport with. Another point to consider is whether they will be too busy to supervise you properly: they might be too snowed under with administration or too involved in conferences and thus may not be able to commit the necessary time to your work.

Whilst doing my PhD, I have also set up my own Internet consultancy. We have had the usual small business start-up problems, but have enjoyed the commercial angle of science and technology. Recent briefs have included consulting for ICL (Kenya), creating an Internet guide to exclusive Indian restaurants, and Internet sites for freight companies.

This dual role means that I work long hours: sometimes from 8.30am to 11pm, including weekends. Work really draws me. I think that to get somewhere one needs to have drive, and to create opportunities for oneself. I have learnt to identify and seize opportunities. I have also recognised the importance of creating alliances and networks that can be of mutual benefit.

Succeeding in science is not easy, but if you are really determined you'll get there. I don't feel I've got 'there' yet by any means, but I look at other women who have made it to the top and try to learn from them.

As for the future, I have the opportunity to carry on with research at university, to join a firm of consultants, or to run my company full-time. I'm not sure which to take up yet, and until I am, I will certainly not close any doors.

Unless otherwise stated, the books listed below are updated on an annual basis. Several are reference books and many of them should be available from your local library. Most of the titles are self-explanatory.

Choosing a course

DOFE: directory of further education

CRAC, Hobsons Publishing plc

A comprehensive reference guide to over 70,000 full-time and part-time FE courses available in the UK.

How to Choose Your Higher National Diploma Course

Trotman

This provides details of courses, entrance requirements and other information.

The Times Good University Guide

Times Books

This details the strengths and weaknesses of all UK universities.

Which University

CRAC, Hobsons Publishing plc

A CD-Rom which can help you to create a shortlist of the universities that might meet your needs. Available on CD-Rom or for further information visit the website: http://www.hobsons.com/whichuni

The PUSH Guide to Which University

PUSH (once the Polytechnic & University Students' Handbook, but now the (P) University Students' Handbook), McGraw Hill

Don't miss this one if you want to know what a particular university is really like! An 'alternative' guide to universities which covers vital issues such as atmosphere, ratios of men to women, strengths and weaknesses, and the percentage of graduates unemployed after six months, all served up in a style that is guaranteed to raise a smile. Also on CD-Rom. Further information is available on email: push@mcgraw-hill.com, and website: http://www.mcgraw-hill.co.uk/push

Which Degree Series

CRAC, Hobsons Publishing plc

The books in this series list all UK full-time and sandwich first degree courses.

Degree Course Guides

CRAC, Hobsons Publishing plc

These provide at-a-glance comparisons of first degree courses in the same subject areas and show how one subject can be treated very differently by different institutions. Information is provided on the course content and teaching methods.

The Complete Degree Course Offers

Brian Heap, Trotman

More vital information: details of offers, admissions and selection procedures in over 700 subject titles in universities and colleges throughout the UK.

UCAS (Universities and Colleges Admissions Service) publishes several useful books, and can also give you further information on applying to university.
UCAS
Fulton House
Jessop Avenue
Cheltenham
Gloucestershire
GL50 3SH
Tel: 01242 222 444; fax: 01242 221 622

UCAS Handbook

UCAS

This handbook lists all the courses at UK universities and provides instructions on when and how to apply to university.

University and College Entrance: the official guide

UCAS

This gives entry requirements, university descriptions, etc.

How to Complete Your UCAS Form

Trotman

The title says it all.

Distance and open learning

The First World Directory of Distance Learning

Open University

Makes available the ICDL (International Centre for Distance Learning) database and open learning course providers worldwide.

Distance and Supported Open Learning UK

Open University

This version concentrates on UK distance learning programmes, with over 2,000 courses at over 200 institutions.

Postgraduate courses

Higher Education in the UK. Graduate Courses

Higher Education Business Enterprise Ltd/ The Times/CVCP/SCOP

A student's guide to postgraduate taught courses at UK universities and higher education colleges.

Postgrad. The Directory of Graduate Studies

CRAC, Hobsons Publishing plc

A comprehensive reference directory of over 20,000 full-time and part-time postgraduate qualifications in the UK.

Postgraduate. The Student's Guide to the Directory of Graduate Studies

CRAC, Hobsons Publishing plc

A condensed version of *The Directory of Graduate Studies* and designed to be a first point of reference on the search for a course.

The Association of MBAs Guide to Business Schools. The Official MBA Handbook

AMBA, Pitman Publishing

A list of places where you can study for an MBA.

Which MBA?

George Bickerstaffe, Addison Wesley, 1995

Subtitled 'a critical guide to the world's best MBA programmes'.

Studying abroad

The European Choice: a guide to opportunities for higher education in Europe

Department for Education and Employment

A short and useful starting point, this booklet is available from the DfEE.

Study Abroad

UNESCO, HMSO

Sources of funding

Check the reference section of your local library to see if they have the following annually updated reference books on sources of funding.

The Directory of Grant-Making Trusts

Written and published by the Charities Aid Foundation

The Educational Grants Directory

John Smyth and Kate Wallace, Directory of Social Change

The Education Funding Guide: support from Government, trusts and companies

edited by Susan Forrester *et al.*, Directory of Social Change, 1995

The Grants Register: the complete guide to postgraduate funding worldwide

Macmillan Press

3

The great race: getting the right job

'However hard you are trying to select women, if they don't apply you can't select them.' Human resources manager in an electricity company

If you enjoy the process of job hunting you are probably in a minority: most people find it a stressful experience, particularly if it involves competing for a single 'glittering' prize against any number of other applicants. You have to keep your sights firmly fixed on the finishing post, and although you might find the race very demanding, remind yourself that the prize has to be won by somebody, and why shouldn't that somebody be you?

It might be helpful to take the analogy of job hunting as a horse race further: focus on one obstacle at a time, and concentrate on getting over it as smoothly as possible. If you do take a tumble, remind yourself that although each race has only one prize worth winning, there are many races and you can keep entering them.

Once again, although there are no guaranteed ways of ensuring you will be the winner, there are ways in which you can reduce your chances of being one of the losers.

Before you line up at the starter's post, you need to be sure that you're in the right race. In other words, in today's highly competitive job market, you will have to be wholeheartedly behind any application you make. You might get as far as an interview, but unless you are a consummate actor, you are unlikely to get any further if you have ambivalent feelings towards the position, the organisation or the work. Make sure you are committed to the application, and that the job you are applying for is worth the time, energy and cost expenditure for you. Naturally at different stages of your life, you will have different criteria you will be weighing up. The SWOT analysis and action plan on pages 14-15 are designed to help you work out where you want to go next from where you are now.

Similarly, an inadequately trained horse may well come a cropper at the first fence. Not only do you need to aim to have the best possible educational qualifications, skills and training, you also need to ensure that those qualifications equip you to run in the race of your choice. The action plan that helps you to select an appropriate educational or training course (page 24) will assist you when you are trying to discover what additional skills and qualifications you need to progress in a particular direction.

The final point seems banally obvious: if you don't stay in the race, there's no chance you can win it. This truism is more significant than it seems: looking at it from employers' point of view, they want to start with the best possible field, and then, through a series of procedures, eliminate the applicants until they are left with a carefully selected handful of contenders from which to choose. The initial advertisement, the mechanical application procedures, the battery of tests, the first stage of interviews and any other selection procedures that lead to the drawing up of a *short* shortlist, have this aim in mind. Therefore at the beginning of the race one of your objectives should be to make sure you are ruled *in*, and not ruled *out*. The advice in this chapter should help you to achieve this.

The job hunting race, then, can be roughly divided into two halves:

- how to get yourself to the stage of being asked for interview
- how not to 'blow it' once you get there.

'Learn the considerable differences between interviewing for industry and for academe. For a research position, both will scrutinize the depth of your research presentation, your teaching experience and skills, how well you work with others, your research plans and your list of publications. But an industrial interviewer will pay close attention to how you will fit as a member of a team in the corporate culture. Any employer will want you to explain how valuable you can be as a scientist or engineer in a variety of positions.' National Academy of Sciences, National Academy of Engineering, Institute of Medicine, USA, Careers in Science and Engineering. A student planning guide to grad school and beyond, 1996, page 99

Getting into the race

In the starting box

First of all, you need to define the parameters of your job search.

- Which jobs do your skills, experience and qualifications equip you for?
- Within those criteria, which type of job would you prefer?
- Which sectors are you prepared to work in?
- What limitations (e.g. geographical, financial) do you need to take into account?

Then you need to find out what's available. Most jobs are advertised; some are not. Accordingly you have to use a variety of strategies to discover what's potentially on offer.

Action Plan: Researching job opportunities

- ❏ Find out which newspapers and journals cover the jobs/sectors that interest you, and consult them as soon as they are published.
- ❏ Make use of electronic information sources: many job vacancies are advertised on the Internet, email, etc.
- ❏ Research the organisations that operate in the areas that interest you, and make a targeted approach to them.
- ❏ Network like mad (see Chapter 4) – the more people who know you are seeking a job, the wider you can spread your net. If you are a member of a professional society or learned institute – use it.
- ❏ Register with your university careers service (if appropriate), local jobcentre, and any employment agencies or headhunters that operate in the right areas.
- ❏ Try some 'informational interviewing' (see below).

Remember:

- ● **Your contacts may be your best chance of obtaining employment.**
- ● **If you fulfil most of the job or promotion specification, don't allow yourself to be intimidated by the skills or experience which you lack: research has demonstrated that men will confidently proceed on the 80% of the required skills that they have, while women will worry about the 20% they lack.**

If you find you are having real difficulty in even obtaining an interview, you probably need extra help, and a career consultant might be able to give you some guidance (see page 67). There are also other strategies you could try. For instance *What Color is Your Parachute?* (see page 185) recommends in detail ways of marketing yourself more effectively, while *To Boldly Go* (see page 58) has a long section on informational interviewing.

'An informational interview is a means of doing research and learning about a particular job, career or organization. It is NOT about getting a job offer – at least not directly. However, ... the contacts, information and encouragement you generally get through an informational interview will very likely lead to a job opportunity.' Peter Fiske, To Boldly Go, 1996, page 61

Informational interviewing is a process in which you investigate your suitability for certain work by arranging to talk to someone who is already doing it. In other words, you approach somebody in an organisation in order to find out more about qualifications and skill requirements and potential opportunities, without there being a job on offer.

If you do arrange an informational interview, you need to treat it as if you were going to a job interview: dress smartly, prepare the questions you would like answers to, and make a point of limiting the time you spend with the person to no more than 30 minutes. Informational interviewing is a way of increasing your knowledge about jobs and companies, making contacts and networking, and also allows you to make a favourable impression. Done well, it can lead on to other openings.

The first hurdle

Once you have identified a job opportunity, your next task is to submit an application which will get you to the initial interview. The following section describes how to construct a positive CV and appropriate letter of application; if you are asked to fill in an application form, adapt this approach to fit the questions on the form.

Information is the key: you need to know as much as possible about the job, the organisation and the people who might interview you. The advertisement and/or job description are your first clues.

Action Plan: Getting an interview

❑ Keep a copy of the advertisement: you will need to consult it when you write your application letter/CV.
❑ If further information or a job description is offered, obtain it.
❑ It can be worth phoning the person concerned to ask for clarification on certain details unless it is indicated that this should not be done.

Before you even start your application, do your homework on the organisation.

❑ Your local library should be able to provide you with further information, and electronic sources of information can be especially useful here. See also page 72.
❑ Access a database of recent reports and newspaper items on the organisation: this can indicate what their current successes, problems and concerns are. (You might then be able to tailor your application to some of these.)
❑ If you are applying to a registered company, you can obtain information about it via Companies House. Telephone 01222 380 801 to find out about the services Companies House can provide.
❑ If the organisation is local, visit its reception area to see whether they have any annual reports, newsletters, etc. which you could have. If it isn't local, most organisations will send out basic information such as annual reports and introductory brochures on request.
❑ If you are applying to an academic institution, you will want to obtain information on relevant research projects and contracts, members of the departments, and so on.

Once again use your contacts. Do you know someone who knows someone who works there?

Equipped with this information, you are then ready to tackle that dreaded CV and letter of application.

Horses for courses: CVs

From the beginning of secondary school and throughout your life, it's useful to build up a database of information on yourself – your skills, educational and professional qualifications, employment history, achievements, publications, research interests, membership of professional societies, and some personal details. (Formal schemes such as those described on page 40 are intended to do this, but there is nothing to stop you creating your own.) You can then use and reuse this database when it comes to making applications, whether these are for jobs, membership of professional societies, voluntary appointments, or whatever.

This information is not your all-purpose CV – in fact if you have 'a' CV that you usually send out, scrap it. You need a 'stable' of CVs, and each CV will be tailored to the position for which you are applying. You can use your database to select (and select is very much the operative word here) the information that is relevant to the position you are seeking, and you will need to create a different type of CV for different situations. Each time, though, you will be revealing what you have achieved and how you have achieved it.

It therefore swiftly becomes clear that there is no 'perfect' CV, either in terms of information, style or format. One personnel officer might respond to an unusual approach; another might use that same approach as a reason to reject the application. Academic CVs carry their own coded messages about desirability via the list of publications, guest lectures, and so on; industrial and business CVs often require a more direct approach.

However, if you imagine someone dealing with piles of applications and – at this stage – looking for the best possible candidates, there are a few general rules which can help you to get your CV onto the 'consider further' pile. You probably know most of them already, but they're worth repeating.

Checklist: Creating a successful CV

❑ Focus on the information that is relevant to the application and consider the order carefully: the more pertinent the information to the job, the higher up the CV it should come.

❑ Accentuate your achievements: don't just list what your positions were but use each 'entry' to reveal how you dealt with a particular challenge, the transferable skills that you have developed, the unique nature of your expertise, or the increasing extent of your seniority. Wherever possible, select the examples which relate to the job in question and which demonstrate comparable or relevant experience.

- ❑ Emphasise the positive and exclude the negative at this stage: if necessary, negative experiences can be dealt with at an interview. For example, don't say why you're job hunting, nor do you need to mention divorce or redundancy, or give details about your health (unless you have a severe disability).
- ❑ Make it *slightly* individual and interesting! A list of jobs, responsibilities, facts and publications may be efficient, but will probably not tell the interviewer the right things about you as a person. What did you *accomplish* in that position?
- ❑ Choose your words carefully: make sure they are positive and dynamic. The list in the box might give you some ideas.

---

achieved, analysed, attained, collaborated, completed, coordinated, created, credited, designed, devised, developed, directed, enabled, established, evaluated, explored, generated, implemented, improved, increased, initiated, led, maintained, managed, mentored, negotiated, organised, participated, persuaded, planned, presented, reduced, resolved, set up, solved, took charge, trained

---

- ❑ Think about including an 'Objective' at the beginning of your CV: a sentence or two about the type of role you are seeking, and the way in which that role would use and develop your existing skills and experience. You might also want to include a short 'Summary' of your career to date.
- ❑ The presentation must be immaculate: if you have to pay to have it typed, do so, but don't pay to have too many printed out for the reasons stated above. It's better to get a few copies printed and the material on disk so that you can adapt the material time and time again. Aim for a simple but elegant design, with a reasonable print size and plenty of space so it's easy to read. Use good quality paper and matching envelopes, and avoid dot matrix printing.
- ❑ The spelling, grammar and so on must be faultless: you might feel that an odd mistake shouldn't matter if you're applying for a highly technical position, but it will indicate a lack of attention to detail and can provide someone with a reason to eliminate your application. Similarly, aim to be consistent in your style (dates, capital letters, job titles and so on).
- ❑ The information should be up-to-date: rewrite your whole CV, don't just tack on a couple of things since you last applied for a job over a year ago.
- ❑ Keep it fairly short (two pages is reasonable) and always relevant: don't waste space with unnecessary items. If you think this is impossible, try some ruthless editing:
  - if you have a degree, you probably don't need to detail your GCSE or even A-level grades:
  - keep personal information to a minimum: do they need to know at this stage whether you are married or have children or that you enjoy reading and going to the cinema?
- ❑ Get someone whose opinion you respect to read your CV. What's their reaction?

Once you have assembled this information in a first draft format, then consider how to slant it towards the position for which you are applying. In his book *To Boldly Go. A practical career guide for scientists*, Peter Fiske demonstrates how this can be done. He provides case studies of six people in which their basic CV is 'restructured' towards different jobs.

Editing your CV

One example Fiske gives in his book is that of Harry Dean Stanchion whose postdoctoral appointment is about to come to an end. Harry's first CV is intended to demonstrate how he has become the 'indispensable' computer guru for the geophysics group at his current university so that his contract can be renewed. The first draft of his CV is more of a comprehensive reference list; it includes too detailed and rather lengthy descriptions of his working history and education, and includes all the jobs he has ever had, including his tutoring experience and even a two-month spell in QUIT Inc!

Harry's second draft is much more focused. Many details have been edited out, and the language is more dynamic. For instance, instead of *'Presented scientific results frequently in both oral and written form including publication in both peer-reviewed journals and electronic media (WWW and E-documents)'*, he has written *'Co-authored 3 papers for publication and presented 4 papers at national and international conferences'*. Similarly *'Volunteer for local school (geoscience lectures, computer advice)'* is transformed into *'Provided educational lectures and computer network advice to local schools'*.

Fiske goes on to describe how whilst working on the amended CV, Harry learns that his CV will be read by the supervisors in the computer support department, not the scientific staff. He consults a friend in a computer hardware company, who advises him to drop the personal interest section and strengthen the objective statement to better fit the potential opening. He also suggests that Harry 'beefs up' his job descriptions and emphasises his project management experience because he knows that the job could develop in this way.

At the same time, Harry's wide range of contacts inform him of a potential opening where he could use his network computing experience outside an academic environment: a commercial real estate company are looking for 'a visionary with excellent computer skills' to initiate a huge Internet marketing programme with multimedia presentations, complex client servers and state-of-art technology. After a telephone conversation with the person concerned, Harry appreciates that the specific skills needed are extensive experience with networked systems, system administration and programming ability in C++ and PERL, and good project management experience. Accordingly, in yet another alternative version of his CV, Harry removes some of the extraneous science and emphasises his networking skills and project management experience even more.

(The above material is adapted from pages 145-50 in *To Boldly Go* by Peter Fiske, published in 1996 by the American Geophysical Union, 2000 Florida Avenue, NW, Washington, DC 20009. For more information you could visit the companion website: http://www.agu.org/careerguide)

Structuring your CV

There are many different ways of structuring your CV, and you will want to choose one or two different structures that you feel comfortable with, and which suit the position for which you are applying. Several computer programmes offer different CV templates. For instance, Word for Windows offers various CV Wizard templates with headings and formats that can be adapted according to whether you want to provide a straightforward chronological CV; a more 'functional' CV which will highlight what you have achieved and the ways in which you have used your skills and experience; or a 'professional' CV which emphasises your professional experience and status and which includes such headings as 'Professional memberships' and 'Patents and publications'.

If you feel you need more information about filling in CVs and application forms, and further examples of different styles and formats, there are several good books available. Try browsing in the appropriate section of your bookshop or library for the approach and style you need. Some useful titles are suggested on page 71.

Application forms

All the points made above apply equally to application forms, and a similar approach can be used. It is best to photocopy the blank application form and fill that in 'in rough' first, as this will help you to produce a more polished final version. Wherever possible, the application form should be typed unless you are requested to complete it in your 'own handwriting'. If you don't type the form, use black ink for ease of photocopying.

Letters of application

Along with your CV or application form, it is customary to include a covering letter 'applying' for the position. This will usually be typed unless the advertisement stipulates otherwise, and should always be sent to a named individual.

Your letter needs to be quite short and succinct: only rarely should it exceed one page in length. Your aim is not to duplicate the information you have supplied elsewhere, but to make the potential employer feel that they will be making a mistake if they do not invite you to an interview. This means that even before you start writing the letter, you need to analyse exactly what their needs are and how you can help to fulfil them.

Most covering letters are three or four paragraphs in length. It is customary to put the job advertised in the title of your letter. You could also add where and when the advertisement appeared, or put this in the first paragraph of your letter along with the other brief, polite formalities (why you are writing, what you are applying for, etc.). The 'meat' of your letter – the second and third paragraphs – should summarise in simple but direct language why and how what you can offer will meet their specific requirements. Try thinking of it in this way: they have a 'problem' which you have recognised, and you are offering them a 'solution'. Brief examples of a relevant job or project can help you to drive home the probability that you are the person they are seeking, whilst you will want to convey the strong but subtle impression that they are the organisation you want to work for.

In the final paragraph you can attempt to 'close the deal' in some way: perhaps by suggesting dates you are (or are not) available for interview, or suggesting some further action. Only do this, though, if it genuinely fits in with your application, or if you are applying to a small organisation or a company without a formal personnel department.

When you are composing this letter, you will want to refer back to the advertisement or job description. It can reinforce the underlying message if you use or modify some of the words and phrases used there in a way that demonstrates that you have understood the organisation's needs – but don't overdo it.

Again, there are examples of covering letters in many books, but it is not wise to adhere to these too rigidly. The whole point of your letter is that you are uniquely suited to this job, and the careful – but not eccentric – individuality of your letter should reinforce that impression.

Finally remember that you will be required to elaborate on the information you have provided in your CV and covering letter if you are invited to an interview, and so you should not only keep copies, but be prepared to discuss any of the information you have supplied in some depth.

Interviewing: how to be 'on form' on the day

With all interviews, find out in advance as much as you can about the place, the interview procedure and the person/people who will be interviewing you. Although an academic interview and an industrial interview might differ in style and format, the key to success will be thorough preparation for the interview, backed up by appropriate knowledge and skills.

Once you have been invited for an interview, you will be facing another series of hurdles which might include any, or all, of the following.

Initial (screening) interview

This is designed to find out more about you, let you find out more about the position, and to see whether you should be considered further – and whether you want to consider the job further.

Once again, in this interview your intention should be to be screened *in* rather than *out*, and this means demonstrating your expertise and knowledge, your understanding of the demands of the job, showing that you would fit in with the culture of the organisation, and raising any 'question marks' the interviewers might have about you in order to deal with them. Again you will need to emphasise that you are part of the solution, not part of a problem.

You should aim to delay discussing salary or conditions as long as possible (preferably leaving it to a later stage) as the keener the employer is on having you, the stronger your negotiating stance will be.

This interview should also allow you to discover whether this job would be right for you.

Subsequent interviews

If you are successful at the first interview, find out what comes next. Will it be:

- a single **one-to-one interview**
- a series of **sequential interviews**, being interviewed by several different people, one after the other, and often being asked the same questions
- or a **panel interview,** where you might be interviewed by any number of people, all firing questions at you?

Each of these types of interviews has its obvious advantages and disadvantages. For example, a panel interview can be quite intimidating, especially if you are put in the 'spotlight chair'. If you know what you are facing in advance, you are less likely to be thrown. Try to adapt your approach: for instance, in a panel interview, look at the person who has asked you the question, but glance quickly round every so often as you answer to include the others in your response. Conversely, in a one-to-one interview you will need to maintain eye contact with the sole interviewer, but in a relaxed manner.

Assessment centres

Along with other candidates, you might be asked to attend an assessment centre for a day or more, where you will be expected to participate in a series of interviews and group discussions and exercises. The aim of the interviewers here is to assess how you function in a simulated working environment.

The exercises you might be put through will vary, but remember that you don't have to 'compete' directly with the other candidates or assume the leadership role to be successful – the interviewers will be watching how you react under pressure, and 'measuring' you on the *contribution* you make. For instance, you can gain brownie points by commenting positively on a suggestion made by another candidate, perhaps then adding your own ideas to develop it. The interviewers may also be assessing how you 'perform' in a supposedly more 'informal' setting – in the bar and over dinner – so relax, but don't relax too much!

If you discover you are expected to do a presentation, prepare it thoroughly, use a few simple but effective visual aids, and practise in advance so that you will be able to complete your presentation within the time allocated.

'I spent two days at the assessment centre. I enjoyed the group exercises because during my GNVQ course we had got used to working in a team. I was also used to doing presentations so that wasn't too much of a problem. There were also a couple of one-to-one interviews where I got the chance to ask some quite detailed questions about the culture of the organisation, the training programme and the MIS (management information systems) that had just been installed.

There were two tasks I found quite difficult. In one, we had to choose between four solutions to an awkward software problem. There wasn't a single right answer, each solution had its drawbacks. The point was we had to make a choice and be able to justify it under tough questioning.

The other task I found daunting was the 'filing tray' exercise, where you had to search through a mass of data and suggest an approach to a particular problem within a specified time. I found this difficult because you had the panic of accuracy combined with the panic of time.' Young computer scientist now working for a High Street bank

Tests

Psychometric tests are used by employers to obtain objective and relevant information about people. They are usually pen and paper tests or questionnaires, although practical exercises are sometimes included.

You may be asked to complete a series of tests, ranging from personality and aptitude tests such as the Myers-Briggs Type Indicator (a personality questionnaire) and the Strong Interest Inventory (which matches interests to careers), to IQ tests, to mathematical or verbal reasoning tests.

With the straightforward personality tests it is advisable to answer the questions as honestly as possible; if you attempt to 'second guess' the answers, you are likely to come unstuck. Besides, would you really be happy as a round peg in a square hole?

However, you can improve your scores on the other tests with practice, and you might feel more confident if you have worked through some of the different tests at home, in a less stressful situation. The books listed on page 71 offer you the chance to practise in advance.

Interview questions

Obviously you will be examined on your knowledge and expertise in your particular SET area – and, if appropriate, you will be expected to defend the conclusions you have drawn from your research, or the way you have tackled a specific SET problem, or how you approached a particular problem in the workplace – but beyond that there are a number of question types that you might encounter in different interview situations. Some examples of possible questions are listed here. However, although you should be prepared to answer these and similar questions, it is important not to 'rehearse' your answers too thoroughly as this can give an artificial impression that could count against you. If you don't know the answer to a specific informational question, it's probably best to admit as much.

Personal questions

Personal questions may be dressed up in different ways, but basically you will be asked about your strengths and weaknesses, and what your approach to the job and the organisation would be. Be prepared for questions along the lines of:

- *Tell us something about yourself.*

Keep it short and relevant.

- *What do you think your particular strengths are?*

Throw modesty out of the window. Pick on one or two strengths that you have which relate to the job in question – go back to your SWOT analysis if necessary (in fact it can be useful to do a SWOT analysis for each job you are being interviewed for) – and give *brief* examples of how you have used these strengths in a comparable challenging situation in the past.

- *What weaknesses/development areas do you have?*

Weaknesses/development areas should be 'turned into' strengths but avoid the clichés like 'I find it difficult to leave work on time'. Instead consider this comment: 'During my first postdoc I realised that I was never going to be a Nobel prizewinner! My strengths were not so much in making significant new discoveries, but in identifying a problem, working out what was needed, and then gathering together a team of experts and brainstorming with them to come up with a viable approach. Armed with that insight, and backed up by that expertise, I am extremely good at designing and setting up the experiments and seeing them through to a fruitful conclusion.' Research immunologist working in industry

- *What do you know about us? Why have you applied for this job?*

If you can't provide an answer to these questions, it is highly unlikely you will be considered for this position.

- *What skills, experience and knowledge do you have which would be useful in this position?*

Your SWOT analysis and the homework you will have done on the organisation will enable you to deal with this question. Use relevant examples from your past wherever possible.

- *What have you learned from your current position?*

Once again, accentuate the positive, and minimise the negative, and use any mistakes to show what you have learned.

- *If we offered you this job, how would you approach it?*

It's essential to be able to answer this question thoughtfully and convincingly.

- *What is your geographical mobility?*

This can be a problem for women – and men – and if this is an issue for you, you will need to have discussed it with your family.

- *Where would you like to be five years from now?*

The honest answer might need to be edited here!

Finally, which is the question you are hoping that they don't ask you? Make sure you are prepared to answer it.

Hypothetical questions

Interviewers often use hypothetical questions to test the extent of your knowledge and experience and to gauge your approach to a specific problem or situation. When possible, relate the problem – or your approach – back to a similar one you have solved in the past.

With these sort of questions, you might want to start by asking the interviewer to define the situation more particularly or checking which aspect of the problem is under discussion – the questions you ask, as well as your answers, can be another way of showing how much you know. Don't, though, fall into the trap of answering every question with a question! It can also be advisable to qualify your answers to hypothetical questions.

Thinking-on-your-feet questions

Unless you have a razor-sharp mind, these can be the most difficult to answer. Questions of this type might include anything and everything, and are structured to find out more about you as a person, and how well you think on your feet and in a stressful situation. Here are a few examples of questions of this type:

- If you could take three things with you on a desert island, what would you take and why?
- Which period of your life would you describe as your happiest, and why?
- Describe yourself from the point of view of your best friend, your worst enemy, and your current boss.
- What makes you feel stressed? Give us a recent example.
- What would you do if you won the Lottery?
- If you could change one thing in the world, what would it be and why?

There are no right answers to these questions. If you can't resist riposting with a quick quip (like the process engineer whose answer to the last question was 'my son's haircut'), fair enough, but perhaps follow it up with a more considered response. Perhaps the best advice here is to be honest. If they don't like the real you, are you going to enjoy working within the organisation anyway?

Your questions

Your questions are an equally important part of the interview and you may be judged almost as much on your questions as your answers – asking a 'good question' is a real skill. At the same time remember that the interviewers are probably committed to a tight and crowded timetable and in some case might not welcome questions, especially complex ones, in the initial selection stages.

Resist the temptation to end an interview with 'I think you've covered all the necessary points'; at the same time don't give them the third degree on salary structures and maternity rights, particularly at an early stage in the selection procedure. Your 'homework' on the organisation and the job will have thrown up various points you want to raise, and there are other, more general things you could ask about such as the culture of the organisation, training opportunities, the experimental facilities that are available, why the position is vacant, future trends and so on. If you feel the atmosphere is right, a brief question on one, or at most two of these points, might be helpful.

Finally, in the stress of your job search, it is very easy to forget that an interview is a two-way process, and *the* important question that an interview should enable *you* to answer is:

'Is this job right for you at this stage of your life?'

Strategies for success

How have other women working in SET survived and thrived in an interview situation?

- 'As a scientist, I approach an interview as a joint problem-solving exercise. You have to reassure the interviewer that you would be part of the solution, and not part of the problem.' Research zoologist

- 'First impressions and body language are incredibly important. It does matter that you dress professionally, smile pleasantly and make eye contact.' Civil engineer

- 'Practice is vital. Ask a friend or colleague to role-play an interview situation or presentation with you. If necessary, get professional help – it's quite a shock when you see yourself on video and you can learn a lot about how you come over to other people. I learned to stop fidgeting and to vary the tone of my voice.' Electrical engineer

- 'Remember that some interviewers are quite inexperienced and you might need to help *them* out. Try saying "You might be interested to know ... " or something along those lines. If you are asked a lot of closed questions [questions with yes or no answers], try to "open" them out.' Materials scientist

- 'When you've answered the question shut up. Don't let the interviewer's silence tempt you into waffling on and ruining a strong point you've just made.' Project manager

- 'If you are being interviewed by a load of senior men, make them think of you as their aunt rather than their niece.' Forensic scientist

- 'Listen carefully to the questions. Too often you think you're being asked a question you've prepared for, and in fact they're asking you something else. If it's a difficult question, take your time to think about it.' Microbiologist

- 'In an interview you will have to sell yourself. Remember they can't read your mind. You are the expert on you, and nobody else will be able to demonstrate as effectively that you are the right person for this job.' Physicist

- 'Be careful not to relax too much once you think the interview's over. A careless comment as you say goodbye can lose you the job. And once the interview's over, don't linger. Make an efficient exit.' Personnel officer

The finishing post

Even if you're first past the finishing post, the process still isn't over. Once you have a job offer in writing – and not before – you will need to negotiate on the salary and conditions of work, and investigate the package of benefits. If the organisation is really keen on appointing you, now is the time to discuss 'your' terms and conditions – six months into the job you might not be in such a strong position. Make sure you know what other people in equivalent positions are getting. Many women find discussing 'what they're worth' embarrassing or are so desperate for any job that they undersell themselves. Don't.

If you receive more than one offer, work out which career path will get you closest to your ultimate goal and/or which organisation best suits you as a person. Go back or telephone and ask questions. You might find that once you tender your resignation, your current employer tries to persuade you to stay. This can make for a difficult choice, but it's worth asking yourself why they offered to promote you/pay you more or whatever, only when you were at the point of leaving.

If you haven't been successful in this race, you will naturally be disappointed and upset. Although you will probably aim to have several irons in the fire at any one time (so that if one application fails you might already be preparing for the next interview), there's no easy way of dealing with 'thank you but no thank you'. Rejections are always a blow.

After you've allowed yourself to get angry, upset or whatever – all very valid reactions – attempt to analyse what you've learned from the experience. Once you've had a chance to recover from your disappointment, it can be worth a phone call to the interviewer requesting some feedback. Good interviewers will accept that you've invested considerable energy and time in this job application and should be happy to talk to you, as long as you approach them positively and make it clear that you are not challenging their decision. Specific questions can assist you to overcome any awkwardness. Try:

- Could you tell me whether there are any qualifications or specific areas of experience where I need to be stronger?
- What feedback could you give me about the way I presented myself in the interview?
- What made you decide in favour of the successful candidate?
- Do you have any opportunities for freelance work/short-term contracts or something similar?
- Is there any specific advice you can offer me which will help me in my career search?

And then you need to put it behind you, learn from it and start thinking about your next application.

Getting stuck

At various stages in your career you might 'get stuck': a spell of unemployment of some sort is becoming a fact of most people's working lives. Crisis points can include getting that all-important first job, being unable to make the next promotion some time in your mid 30s, re-entering the job market after a career break, and keeping up the career momentum in your late 40s or early 50s.

You can overcome these problems with a combination of:

- forward action planning
- dogged determination
- refining your job application and interview skills
- building up your skills and qualifications through specific education or training courses (see Chapter 2)
- intense and continuous networking (see Chapter 4)
- broadening your experience and expertise by working in a different area, or if necessary in a voluntary capacity which will not only keep you in circulation but also enable you to develop key skills (see Chapter 9 on involvement in public life)
- and expert careers counselling.

Careers guidance is something that can be useful at all stages of your career. If you have limited financial resources, your nearest adult careers guidance service might be the best place to start (your local library or citizens' advice bureau should be able to provide you with the telephone number), or try the National Helpline for Careers Guidance, available from Autumn 1997.

If you have studied at a university, find out whether that entitles you to use its careers service for life.

If you can afford it, you might find an in-depth assessment with a specialist careers counsellor useful – and again your adult careers guidance service can probably help you. (If you are unfortunate enough to be made redundant, you could ask for free sessions as part of the severance package.) This might involve a series of personality tests and an extensive one-to-one counselling session, with a written report. Other forms of counselling might be expert advice on CVs, application forms, and interview techniques to enable you to take that next step forward. This was the experience of the metallurgist in the following profile.

'I think for many scientists the crunch comes at around 35. There's a lot of mobility at the bottom and sufficient mobility at the top, but not much in the middle. I'd applied for promotion both within the company and outside, and after a series of rejections I realised I needed to do something different if I was going to move on.

Rather embarrassedly, I consulted a careers consultant. She worked on my interview techniques with me, and by using videos and analysis, helped me to see that I was coming across in the wrong way. She also showed me that I was expecting the interviewers to understand what I could offer, and that I needed to spell out the benefits of why I should work for them. With her help, I managed to make the move I wanted. Interestingly, once I felt more confident and revealed to others that I had taken advice, many of my new colleagues admitted they had done something similar.' Metallurgist

Many of the regional careers services now also offer services such as personal consultation, CV production, psychometric testing and in-depth interviews and reports, but you will usually have to pay more for these services.

From the other side of the desk

How do employers see the recruitment process, and what advice would they offer to women in SET? Here are some comments from personnel officers and others on the other side of the interviewing desk.

- 'What am I looking for in an interview? Evidence of motivation, a real interest in the profession and the work, and a keenness to develop. We also need people who are good team players, with strong communication skills coupled with a good sense of humour.'

- 'People assume you understand what they've done just from a job title. They don't explain their achievements.'

- 'At times I have to hunt through pages and pages of CV to find out what I need to know.'

- 'Things like spelling are important on an application form, because the research itself demands attention to detail.'

- 'This is a sweeping generalisation, but women do tend to undersell themselves. I often have to probe quite deeply before I can form a view of their achievements.'

- 'Be prepared. Find out about the company. Think about what you've done and what you can offer.'

- 'If we advertise a position we get hundreds of CVs in response. Candidates should try to make the job of the selector as easy as they can. They should tailor their application to the position they wish to apply for.'

What comes over from employers time and time again is that all other things being equal, what they are seeking is a genuine enthusiasm for the job: that elusive spark of passion which can ignite a successful partnership between employee and employer; in other words, they are looking for someone that will enjoy working within the organisation and who will get on with other members of the team.

Professor Felix Franks, managing director of a biotechnology company and university professor

Professor Felix Franks has had extensive experience of interviewing and recruiting scientists during his long career which has encompassed working for large multinationals such as Unilever, managing a young and expanding biotechnology company, and teaching and researching in universities in both the UK and abroad. He offers the following insights into the recruitment process.

The only thing you've got to go on is what comes in the post – the letter and application form or CV. From that you have to make a judgement, and applicants have to accept that the person reading their application might be prejudiced for or against it, and that that prejudice might be quite irrational.

When you are applying for a job, you should aim to get close to the specific requirements of the position, but you don't have to have them all. For one job we requested a foreign language, but the four people who stood out didn't have that skill and we eventually appointed someone who couldn't offer another language but who was prepared to start learning one.

Your application should be well organised and legible, and not too long and wordy. I will accept the occasional spelling mistake, but when I received an application from someone who described himself as a 'Principle scientific officer', I rejected it. If he couldn't even spell his own job title correctly ...

One application I received from a young scientist was so well organised I could immediately form a picture of her. There weren't too many words and every word counted. She had obviously had a career in mind for some time and had chosen her course of study carefully. All her vacation work was geared to acquiring the experience that would help her career. She interviewed well too: she had presence. I knew I would be happy to let her go out to clients and represent the company quite early on. She got the job. I found out later that she was one of eight children and that she had taken on a lot of responsibilities within the family from a young age. It showed.

At an interview you need to demonstrate what you've done and let the interviewer form their own view of your achievements. Let *them* work out how good you are.

In an interview situation, whether in industry or academia, I am looking for various criteria. Obviously applicants need to be able to do the job or the research, but beyond that, I want to know whether they are articulate: simple things such as do they finish their sentences? I expect them to have done their homework and have something worked out about their career aspirations, and to be able to ask me intelligent questions about the position and the organisation. When I ask them about their interests, I like to feel that they have really thought about it and don't just trot out rote answers.

These factors are true for both industry and academia, but there are obviously differences too. For instance, one of the questions I often ask is: 'What area of research would you pursue if you had complete freedom of choice?' Within an industrial context, I am always depressed if someone responds that they would carry on with their PhD research, but in a university environment, this is a perfectly acceptable answer.

From my experience of the bio-industry and pharmaceutical sector, I think that today women start with advantages. They seem more mature than men at an earlier age, are better organised and handle themselves effectively. They dress well. They appear to be more articulate. However, I do not think you can extrapolate to other sectors: I imagine this might not be true in heavy engineering. But in recent years when I've been sifting through applications, I find it's not shortlisting women that's the problem, but shortlisting men.

Not surprisingly, there are many books on the market that deal with CVs, interviews and job search strategies. It's worth browsing in your library or local bookshop, perhaps looking out for the following titles, most of which are self-explanatory.

Job applications

How to Find the Perfect Job: a step-by-step guide

Tom Jackson, Piatkus, 1993

Perfect Job Strategies: over 100 proven strategies for getting the job you want in today's challenging market

Tom Jackson, Piatkus, 1994

The Perfect CV: how to get the job you really want

Tom Jackson and Ellen Jackson, Piatkus, revised edition 1996

The Perfect CV: all you need to get it right first time

Max Eggert, Arrow Business Books, 1992

The Perfect Interview: all you need to get it right first time

Max Eggert, Arrow Business Books, 1992

Tests

How to Pass Selection Tests

Mike Byron and Sanjay Modha, Kogan Page, 1991

How to Pass Technical Selection Tests

Mike Byron and Sanjay Modha, Kogan Page, 1993

How to Pass Graduate Recruitment Tests

Mike Byron and Sanjay Modha, Kogan Page, 1994

How to Pass Computer Selection Tests

Sanjay Modha, Kogan Page, 1994

How to Pass Verbal Reasoning Tests

Harry Tolley and Ken Thomas, Kogan Page, 1996

How to Master Psychometric Tests

Mark Parkinson, Kogan Page, 1997

Test Your Own Aptitude

Jim Barrett and Geoff Williams, Kogan Page, 2nd edition 1990

Great Answers to Tough Interview Questions: how to get the job you want

Martin John Yate, Kogan Page, 3rd edition 1992

Clever answers to difficult questions, but such a bestseller that the interviewers have all read it too, so bear that in mind!

Readymade Interview Questions

Malcolm Peel, Kogan Page, 2nd edtion, 1996

It can also be illuminating to look at the recruitment process from the interviewer's point of view. *Readymade Interview Questions* and the further books it recommends, will enable you to do just that.

Doing your homework

The British Library Science Reference and Information Service (SRIS) publishes a 'How to Find Information' series as part of its services to science, technology and industry. These comprehensive guides to the published resources available are very useful if you are trying to find out more about a company! Telephone 01462 672 555 for distribution details. The titles include:

How to Find Information: Business. A guide to searching in public sources

How to Find Information: Chemistry. A guide to searching in public sources

How to Find Information: Life Sciences. A guide to searching in public sources

How to Find Information: Environment. A guide to searching in public sources

How to Find Information: Medicine and Biology. A guide to searching in public sources

How to Find Information: Engineering. A guide to searching in public sources

4

A helping hand: mentoring and networking

'For many of these [female] scholars a crucial role in the launching of their careers was played by a mentor, often an enlightened man, who spurred them on, gave them a break or just treated them as another intellectual ... the abiding message is that we all must take responsibility for encouraging and nurturing the gifts or others, wherever we have the opportunity.' Helena Kennedy, Beyond the Glass Ceiling, 1996, page 8

Mentoring

What is a mentor?

*'**Mentor**. A guide, a wise and faithful counsellor; so called from Mentor, a friend of Ulysses, whose form Minerva assumed when she accompanied Telemachus in his search for his father.'* Brewer's Concise Dictionary of Phrase & Fable, 1993, page 666

Most people benefit from encountering role models of what they would like to be, and this can be especially useful when the exemplary person is someone you know and can talk to. The concept of mentoring grows out of this idea and formalises, to varying degrees, a particular kind of mutually helpful interaction. Usually it's a younger person testing ideas and getting advice from a more experienced and knowledgeable person, but it's not all give on one side and all take on the other. There are benefits for both mentees and mentors.

In the USA there have been both official and unofficial mentoring structures in academic and business organisations for some time. It is only in recent years that the idea of mentoring in a more formal way has begun to win cautious acceptance and approval within the UK. Many people are still unfamiliar with the concept, and there are different ideas about what a mentor should be and should do. For instance:

- 'A good mentor should offer help, advice, support and encouragement and a possible role model to inspire others. Mentoring is a nurturing, one-to-one relationship.' Civil engineer

- 'Being mentored is about learning and acquiring skills and expertise in different areas: professional, social and technical.' Project manager

- 'A mentor should ask you questions and challenge you.' Professor of biophysics

- 'A mentor is a skilled counsellor, often somebody in your organisation, who can give you guidance about how your career might develop and suggest what you should be aiming for and what you need to do next. They can also be a friend.' Industrial chemist

- 'An effective mentor will see you and your career in the context of the whole person and can give you guidance accordingly.' Research immunologist

- 'A good mentor can be a short cut to success – somebody who can save you from making expensive mistakes and who can help you to develop solutions to personal and career problems.' Mechanical engineer
- 'A mentor is someone who encourages you to believe in yourself.' Quality control analyst
- 'A mentor is someone who believes in you more than you do in yourself.' Research biologist

A mentor can and should be some or all of these things.

Within a university or research institute, your supervisor, head of department or section might function as a mentor; in industry, your line manager might be your mentor. Whoever they are, your mentor should assist you to advance your career.

'I have had two pieces of valuable advice and help from two male mentors.

The first was back in 1949 when I was coming up to finalising my PhD work. My professor said to me: "Why not go to America and do a postdoc?" The practice of postdoccing in America had barely emerged at the time, and the idea had certainly not occurred to me. He advised me how to go about it. I followed his advice and doing a postdoc in America at that stage of my career was one of the best things I could have done.

The second was after I'd taken a career break of eight years, and my youngest child was four and just starting school. Another senior scientist suggested I apply for a personal research fellowship and offered to support my application to do my own work and publish in my own name. Again, this was the best thing I could have done at the time.

The advice to "Publish, publish, publish – but only worthwhile material," is something I have passed on to many of my own mentees.' Research chemist

The benefits of being mentored

As well as all the advantages listed in the different definitions of a mentor, you should hope to gain some or all of the following benefits from an effective mentor in a university environment, whether it's your PhD supervisor or a senior academic. They should:

- provide up-to-date guidance and advice about your initial choice of research area and its subsequent direction
- be prepared to comment on drafts of articles for journals and conference papers and suggest where they might best be published (it goes without saying they will be commenting on your PhD!)

- boost your confidence and be encouraging
- discuss where you might go and what you might do next
- point you in the right direction for information about funding sources
- advise you on grant proposals and funding applications
- assist you to identify and take advantage of opportunities for participation in scientific and professional conferences, seminars and meetings
- actively put you into contact with other researchers/significant people/projects in your field.

'I suppose you could call my supervisor a mentor when I was doing my PhD in physical chemistry. I would go to him full of enthusiasm and explain my brilliant idea. He would comment: "So what?" I would be forced to elaborate. "So what?" I would develop my arguments. "So what?" If I got past four "So whats?" I knew I had an idea worth working on.' Professor of biophysics/managing director of a biotechnology company

Within a company, your expectations might be slightly different but you should still hope to get similar help and guidance from your manager or mentor, as well as a helping hand up the career ladder (or the drainpipe!). Any manager in industry or academia should recognise potential and help develop that potential for the benefit of the individual and the organisation.

A good mentor can make all the difference to your career.

'Many people have support from their families or their partners in their careers but this is not the case for everybody. For some people, a mentor is an important source of career support. When a top physicist I met at a conference told me that he believed I was on the right track, and that I should go forward when I was thinking of turning back, it made me change my mind.' Physicist

What to look for in a mentor

Within some organisations, you might have an officially appointed mentor; in others, there might be an informal mentoring process or you might have to find your own 'unofficial' mentor. If your organisation does not have a formal mentoring system, you could look for a mentor through your immediate contacts: ask your colleagues for suggestions, follow up any discussions that seem to tend in a mentoring direction, and if someone offers to give you advice on a specific subject or comment on some of your work, make a point of taking them up on it. Joining a professional society (see page 83) could be another avenue to explore.

Whether formal or informal, what are the qualities you might want to look for in a mentor?

Checklist: The qualities of a good mentor

A good mentor could be someone who:

- ❏ will consider all your discussions to be in the strictest confidence
- ❏ is reasonably available and accessible
- ❏ has good communication skills
- ❏ possesses information, experience and judgement which you do not yet have
- ❏ understands the politics of the organisations and environment in which you are operating or might wish to work, and can advise you 'how to play the game'
- ❏ can appreciate the problems and obstacles which you might encounter
- ❏ helps you to identify your weaknesses and to develop strategies to overcome them
- ❏ empowers you to work out your own solutions
- ❏ can provide an objective view to help you think through the options
- ❏ you respect, and who respects you.

As well as a fair proportion of the benefits listed above, a good mentoring relationship will focus on your professional and personal needs, and provide you with:

- ❏ increased self-confidence, support and the courage to move forward
- ❏ a greater knowledge of the organisation in which you are working, as well as some appreciation of its politics
- ❏ the opportunity to meet the people who can influence your career and develop your networks.

Conversely, if your mentor is not providing you with enough of these benefits and support – or if, quite simply, you do not get on together – you should either look for a new mentor, or seek someone who can provide you with the additional guidance that you are lacking: you may need more than one mentor at any one time, reflecting the different areas and needs of your life and your career.

Two potentially problematic aspects of mentoring which are often raised are the geographical proximity of the mentor and their gender. Neither of these factors should be a disadvantage and indeed could be a plus factor.

'The person who has helped me most with my career lives and works in another country, but we communicate regularly by email and telephone, and meet up at conferences.' Physicist

Similarly, although you might prefer to have a mentor of the same sex, it could be unwise to make this an overriding factor. Apart from the lack of available senior women mentors in many areas of SET and academia, obstacles and problems you might experience could be due to your age or personality or lack of experience, rather than to the fact that you are a woman.

'All my mentors have been male. There weren't any women around.' Production support engineer

Moving on: being a mentor yourself

As your career progresses, you will probably notice that the balance shifts and you yourself may become a mentor. If so, you might perhaps question whether you can afford to give up yet more of your all-too precious time. Happily, most people who become mentors find that it is very much a two-way process and they get a great deal out of it:

- 'I find mentoring challenging: I like dealing with brilliant young minds. When I'm asked difficult questions, it sharpens my own thinking. ' Professor of mathematics

- 'I enjoy it. I like the young woman I am mentoring, and as well as discussing the serious issues, we have a laugh and a chat – and sometimes a drink in the pub.' Chemical engineer

- 'I have enhanced some of my own skills through mentoring young engineers: these include communication skills, counselling and teamwork.' Project manager

- 'I am glad that my mentees can learn from the mistakes that I have made and I get satisfaction from helping others to develop.' Civil engineer

- 'Being a mentor is a link into the next generation and into new ways of working and thinking. I feel I am giving something back.' Hydrogeologist

- 'Mentoring is a good way of identifying young and able people to work with you.' Professor of chemistry

- 'I've decided that my next career step will be out of research into management. I find I am now being an informal mentor to the researchers under me, and as they increase their skills and expertise, I can delegate more to them and this leaves me freer. In this way, as well as advancing their career, I am advancing my own.' Telecommunications consultant

Even so, on occasions even the most altruistic mentor may need recharging: 'As an American, I've been both an official and unofficial mentor for many different people, both male and female, over the years and I've gotten a lot out of it. But every so often – usually on a Friday afternoon – I've had enough and feel like saying "Hey, let's talk about me for a change!" ' Marketing director of a computer company

If you feel like this, don't neglect yourself. Even a mentor can benefit from having a mentor.

National Mentoring Consortium

The National Mentoring Consortium operates a mentor scheme for African, Caribbean and Asian undergraduates. It supports undergraduates from ethnic minorities by offering them positive role models, and by helping them to find good work placements and graduate traineeships. The National Mentoring Consortium helps individual universities to run local mentor schemes by acting as a link between them and the employer contacts, and by providing the expertise and training.

National Mentoring Consortium
University of East London
Romford Road
London
E15 4LZ
Tel: 0181 590 7000 extension 4343; fax: 0181 849 3646

The University of Edinburgh Science and Engineering Mentoring Programme

In the Faculty of Science and Engineering and Technology at the University of Edinburgh, only 7% of senior lecturers and 4.7% of professors are women. Previous research has suggested that senior female staff can make an important contribution in encouraging young women to realise their potential. Consequently the University is now running a mentoring and development programme aimed primarily at women staff and a limited number of postgraduate students, to complement the existing mentoring programme run within the University for undergraduates. The programme links women near the beginning of their careers in SET with more senior women, and aims to set up a formal mechanism to encourage more senior women to provide advice and guidance on developing research ideas, seeking funding, teaching and administration to more junior colleagues. It is important that the mentor may also be able to provide more personal assistance on the issues many women face in terms of decisions about family and children. For further information contact:

The Project Director
Science and Engineering Mentoring Programme
University of Edinburgh Careers Service
33 Buccleuch Place
Edinburgh
EH8 9JT
Tel: 0131 650 4670; fax: 0131 650 4479; email: Isabel.Turnbull@ed.ac.uk

If I Can You Can

If I Can You Can is a voluntary project set up in Sheffield to challenge stereotypes about women and the modern working environment. It provides a role model and mentoring scheme linking students in local schools and women from a variety of backgrounds. The aims are to motivate young people – and particularly young women – to reach for choices which may seem initially to be beyond them, to encourage positive achievement, and to demonstrate the important role of women at work and in the community. If you would like to be a mentor, telephone If I Can You Can at the Sheffield Education Business Partnership on 0114 272 7544.

Dorothy Hodgkin Fellows (see page 152) are offered a mentor from outside the department in which they are working so that they can bounce ideas off them, and receive careers guidance.

The Daphne Jackson Memorial Fellowships Scheme (see page 133), and many educational and training courses (particularly those aimed at women returners) recognise the importance of someone who fulfils the role of a mentor.

Networking

'I'm a compulsive networker.' Research chemist

Everyone knows about the serendipity factor – the good luck to be in the right place at the right time – but you increase your chances of that happening if you actively participate in informal networks. You probably do already.

Defined simply, a 'network' is a group of people who have something in common and who are prepared to help each other and let others help them. Career-wise, we may not quite have reached the stage of 'network or die', but we are certainly very near to it! Unfortunately some women are still hesitant about 'networking' as they feel it smacks of 'using' people and they are reluctant to 'exploit' their friends and other contacts. Yet, in the positive sense of the word, women have been networking for centuries: exchanging stories and information about childbirth, looking after each others' children, and passing on particularly effective remedies for illnesses. Writers' groups, babysitting circles, sports clubs, old friends from undergraduate days and volunteers working for charities are all instances of networking, as well as formal and informal work-related groups. If you phone up a friend about an advert you've seen or mention that an old schoolmate would like your vacation job next summer, you are networking. What is more, the lessons you have learned about networking in other areas of your life will be valuable in the professional sphere.

When it comes to careers, it won't take you long to discover that 'what you know' is seldom enough on its own; 'who you know' can be a critical success factor while 'who knows you know what you know' is even more vital. Effective networking will provide you with access to information, advice and training, and, hopefully, encouragement as well, especially if you encounter some successful role models. A strong network (or networks) will enable you to learn from other people's experiences, and allow other people to learn from you. By pooling often-scarce resources through a network, you may also find that you can campaign for improvements in conditions, or changes in policies relating to your and others' living and working conditions, more effectively. On a social level, networks can add another dimension to your life – like mentoring, networking can be fun.

There are many ways in which networks can help you to progress: for instance, a well-timed drink in the local can help you to find out who is leaving, and which jobs are therefore going to become vacant. Many people testify to the ways in which networking in one form or another has helped them:

- 'When I first started working as an electronic engineer I felt quite isolated and unusual. Networking with other women in the same field through my professional society reduced that sense of isolation.' Electronic engineer

- 'I'm not a conference goer – sitting around being chatty is not my thing – but I have built up my networks through research collaboration and I use these on a regular basis.' Chemical engineer

- 'I have acquired a great deal of information about grant-awarding bodies and grant application procedures through both my formal and informal networks.' Research oceanographer

- 'I'm a self-employed computer training consultant, and I get most of my work by word-of-mouth recommendations – by networking, in other words.' Computer consultant

Formal and informal networks

You may be a member of several different networks at any one time. Some of those networks may be formal and some informal; all are valuable. It can prove worthwhile to attend your professional society's annual conference, but a quick lunch with a girlfriend or your old boss or a university colleague and a chat about who's doing what where might be equally useful – the importance of informal networks should not be underestimated. Your networks may overlap, or cover completely separate spheres of your life. It may be that a member of your badminton club mentions a job vacancy at their company which would suit you down to the ground, or that a member of your university department is in the same babysitting circle.

The Useful Addresses on page 207 onwards and throughout this book include some of the organisations and networks you might find valuable. Some women feel more comfortable with women-only networks and so several of these are listed.

Postal and electronic networks

Postal and electronic networks are extremely important for scientists and engineers working in today's 'global village' and by this time everyone working in SET must be familiar with the swift international exchange of ideas and information over the Internet, the World Wide Web and email. These are valuable sources of international networking opportunities, and you will no doubt wish to take full advantage of them. Again, electronic networks are included in the list of Useful Addresses.

Setting up your own network

'If the network you need doesn't exist, start it.' Industrial pharmacologist

At times you may find that you need to develop a network to meet a specific need. Often this can involve you consciously networking with your own interests in mind in order to evolve another network: you can be sure that if you need it, someone else will too. After all, most of the established networks and organisations that are around today started for just those reasons. The following organisations are examples of networks that became established in response to a need.

African-Caribbean Network for Science & Technology

The African-Caribbean Network for Science & Technology was formed as 'a result of the dismay of black scientists and engineers at the marked under-representation of black people in SET institutions in the UK'. It is a national network of African-Caribbean professionals working for the advancement of the educational and career aspirations of African-Caribbean people of all ages, in science, technology, engineering, medicine and other related fields. The Network aims to increase the number of and provide educational and career support to African-Caribbean youngsters and adults wishing to develop careers in these areas, to offer positive role models and school and workplace mentors, and to provide a forum for debate. For further information contact:

African-Caribbean Network for Science & Technology
Ishango House
447 Chester Road
Old Trafford
Manchester
M16 9HA
Tel: 0161 877 1480; fax: 0161 877 1481

Association for Women in Science and Engineering (AWiSE)

Not to be confused with the Engineering Council's WISE campaign, AWiSE is a national organisation with an office in London and branches in the regions. AWiSE was founded in 1994, following the publication of *The Rising Tide* (see page 19), to advance the participation of girls and women in science and engineering, and to contribute to the formulation of policy in these fields. Its purpose is to act as a forum, a network for mutual support, a centre of information and resource, and a collective voice for women in science and engineering in the broadest sense, covering the sciences and technologies at all levels, including education, research, industry, administration and the media.

A number of branches and regional groups have sprung up, their activities including talks, discussions, meetings, events and career workshops, with rapid news transmission through electronic mail, and the chance to exchange views, experiences and career strategies. Information is available via the website http://www.awise.org or contact:

AWiSE National Office
1 Park Square West
London
NW1 4LJ
Tel: 0171 935 3282/5202; fax: 0171 935 0736; email: awise@wellcome.ac.uk

Women's Engineering Society (WES)

It was 'a sense of isolation in a male-dominated environment' that led to the formation of the WES in 1919 with the aim of helping other women to become engineers. Verena Holmes, who became the first woman to be a full member of the Institution of Mechanical Engineers, Dame Caroline Haslett, who started the Electrical Association for Women in the 1920s, and Amy Johnson, the pioneer aviator, are amongst the society's past presidents. Today WES is still 'promoting the education, training and practice of engineering among women' and aims to 'raise the profile and effectiveness of women engineers by forming links and networking with other women's organisations'. WES offers advice and information to anyone interested in the role of women in engineering and science and is particularly keen to increase company membership to support women and their employers within the workplace. Contact WES at:

Imperial College of Science, Technology and Medicine
Department of Civil Engineering
Imperial College Road
London
SW7 2BU
Tel: 0171 594 6025; fax: 0171 594 6026; email: wes@ic.ac.uk

Professional and learned societies

Formal networks often take the form of a professional or learned society and there are many of these within SET, often long-established. Some professional societies have a women-only committee or section (such as the Women Chemists' Committee of the Royal Society of Chemistry and the Women in Physics Group of the Institute of Physics) and while some people may feel that single-sex groups are no longer appropriate, it is up to each individual to make their own judgement. In any case, many women within SET find it useful, if not essential, to join appropriate professional societies. The names of many of the professional societies in SET are included in the Useful Addresses on pages 207-212, but bear in mind that the list is not exhaustive, but 'indicative'.

The following checklist suggests some of the benefits that a professional society might offer you.

Checklist: Professional societies – best practice

What could/should a professional society offer you? You may require:

- ❑ a way of meeting and maintaining contact with other professionals in either your geographical area or area of expertise
- ❑ informal/social meetings at regional levels
- ❑ a means of keeping up to date with developments in the field – through journals, conferences, seminars, or informed talks
- ❑ women's sections for those who prefer them
- ❑ support and mentoring schemes, either formal or informal
- ❑ continuing professional development (CPD) training and other career activities, and the opportunity to take the necessary exams and/or qualify for full professional status even if you take a career break or do not work full-time
- ❑ active lobbying of employers, for instance to improve access to childcare, to facilitate the return of women to work on a part-time or flexible basis, and the removal of age restrictions
- ❑ reduced subscriptions for members who are on a career break or retired
- ❑ information on revised codes of practice
- ❑ the chance to have input into governmental and other decision-making bodies.

As previously mentioned, the international aspects of SET are crucial. It can be valuable to join, for example, a North American or European professional society, as this is an effective way of staying up to date with developments in other countries, keeping in touch with overseas colleagues, and finding out about forthcoming conferences, or grants and awards for which you might be eligible.

Pam Liversidge, mechanical engineer and President of the Institution of Mechanical Engineers

Among other things, Pam Liversidge's career to date has encompassed the 'blood sweat and tears' of financing and setting up her own engineering company in Sheffield (manufacturing specialist metal powders) and several years as an executive and engineer in the forging industry during which time she built and ran a forge to manufacture turbine and compressor blades. She serves in a voluntary capacity on the board of governors of Sheffield Hallam University and as a director of Sheffield TEC. Pam Liversidge is also a visiting professor at the University of Sheffield.

I first became involved in my professional institution about 15 years ago when I went along to some lectures on technological developments in the aerospace industry organised by the local branch of the Institution of Mechanical Engineers. It wasn't long before I was branch treasurer and secretary for the Yorkshire region! Eventually at the behest of the branch I stood for election to the governing council of the Institution and was elected at the first attempt.

Since then I have been a deputy president and vice president, and in May 1997 I took up the presidency of the Institution of Mechanical Engineers. It is 150 years since the foundation of the Institution and the appointment of a woman president in the anniversary year marks the increased role of women in the profession. Obviously within the last century and a half, life has moved on tremendously, and the function of a 'learned society' has similarly evolved. Now people have less 'disposable' time and a greater number of possible ways of spending it, and so the learned societies have to broaden their appeal if they are to survive. We need to do this by meeting the needs of our members, whether these needs are professional, educational or social.

Over the years I have had a variety of commitments outside my 'career', and I always think long and hard before I take them on. Whether a post is paid or voluntary, you need to be able to do it properly, and should be prepared to give 'quality time' to it. In return, becoming involved in an organisation such as your professional institution can develop you as an individual, and hone your presentation and organisational skills, as well as expand your networks. It is really important for women in business and industry to work at their networks – often the 'dividend' is a long-term benefit. Frequently jobs or positions come through personal recommendation so it is important to have a reasonably high profile.

During my career I have been mentored by several senior male colleagues and it has been invaluable. I try now to do the same for younger people, male and female. This was a very satisfying part of my role as head of strategic planning at East Midlands Electricity.

The challenge of the presidency is one that I find a little daunting, but exciting. It will take up three to four days a week. I am most fortunate in that my husband and I own our own group of engineering manufacturing businesses which are managed on a day-to-day basis by full-time executives. Consequently for this special year I have become non-executive but still get a salary, as the presidency is an unpaid position. It will involve extensive international travel – for instance, I have been asked to deliver the keynote speech at the centenary celebrations of the Japanese Society of Mechanical Engineers in Tokyo, and I will also be speaking in Singapore. The presidency is not something that I shall ever do twice, and my hope is that I will do it well enough so that the Institution will be glad to elect another woman to its highest office at a future date.

Networking and Mentoring: a woman's guide

Dr Lily M. Segerman-Peck, Piatkus, 1991

An excellent book which covers in detail the benefits of networking and mentoring. It gives expert guidance on what to look for in a mentor, selecting a mentor who is right for you, and getting the most out of being mentored. It also tackles some of the problems that can arise in a mentoring relationship and goes on to discuss how you can become an effective mentor for others and/or set up a mentoring scheme. It includes interesting case studies and real-life examples, and a comprehensive bibliography.

Coaching, Mentoring and Assessing: a practical guide to developing competence

Eric Parsloe, Kogan Page, revised edition 1995

Using a practical approach with checklists, case studies, and 'how to' sections, this book is aimed at managers, trainers and consultants interested in staff development.

The Mentoring Manager

Gareth Lewis, The Institute of Management Foundation/Pitman Publishing, 1996

Subtitled 'Strategies for fostering talent and spreading knowledge' and described as 'an interactive programme for bringing out the best in your staff', this book is primarily intended for managers who are interested in establishing a mentoring programme, but it has useful information about the expectations and demands of the mentor–learner relationship.

Women's Organisations in the United Kingdom: a directory

Published, written by and obtainable from the Women's National Commission (address on page 199)

A useful source of information about the range of women's organisations in the UK. Updated biennially.

Adviser, Teacher, Role Model, Friend - on being a mentor to students in science and engineering

National Academy of Sciences, National Academy of Engineering, Institute of Medicine, USA, National Academy Press, 1997

Very focussed, with useful checklists, etc.

5

Having it all? balancing career and family responsibilities

'Rather than thinking of marriage and parenthood as having a fixed effect on women scientists' careers, we should see them as a set of problems and opportunities. Women scientists are faced with the dilemma of "synchronizing" the often conflicting demands of three clocks: their biological clock, their career clock (such as their tenure clock), and their spouse's career clock. On the other hand, a husband and a family can provide emotional security and financial stability as well as scientific support if the husband is a scientist in the same field. Largely depending on how the problems are resolved and the opportunities used, the effect of marriage and children on women scientists' careers may be positive or negative.' Gerhard Sonnert, Who Succeeds in Science? The gender dimension, 1995, page 162

Can you 'have it all'?

And if you can't have it all, can you have 70 or 80 or 90%?

Today many women rightly expect to share in the benefits that having a professional career can bring; similarly many men expect to share in the benefits offered by a fuller life outside work and a greater involvement with their family's daily lives. But how realistic are these aims? Who succeeds in realising them? And to what extent do female scientists and engineers have to face specific issues and problems which might make it particularly difficult for them to achieve a balance in their lives?

All the women featured throughout this book enjoy their work and their lives outside their work. It *is* possible to have some of the best of both worlds. Careers in science, engineering and technology have a number of advantages when it comes to balancing work and home.

- A career in SET can do wonders for your self-esteem. It can be very stimulating and intellectually challenging, and this can benefit you as a partner and a mother.
- The financial rewards are often good. Scientists and engineers are frequently well paid, and this can help you to obtain the back-up help you might require.
- With good qualifications and experience, you are unlikely to suffer long periods of unemployment.
- You might be relatively mobile in terms of employment opportunities, on both a national and international basis.
- Mothers who work in an academic environment often discover that their work patterns can dovetail conveniently with school terms.
- Because SET professionals are in demand, you may be able to work part-time or flexible hours (if this is what you wish to do) without having to accept a drop in status and working conditions.
- Women can and do become high flyers in SET – as several of the profiles in this book demonstrate.

However, at the same time there are a number of problems which you might experience during your career. None of these, though, are unique to SET, and all can be overcome.

Once again, it's a case of working out what's right for *you*, and you can approach this in the same way as you would tackle a scientific experiment or an engineering problem. After all, combining a career and family:

- is another form of problem-solving
- is amenable to data analysis (what are your resources?)
- needs rational thought (to supplement the emotional realm which no one would deny)
- and requires planning.

Naturally luck and circumstances will play a large role, and if everything seems to be falling into place, ignore this chapter – if it's not broken don't fix it! But for many women, the issues of career and family life are some of the most rewarding and challenging they will tackle. It can be a very creative and positive experience to think about those issues and discuss them with those closest to you, whether they are your partner, your friends or your children.

So what problems might you and other women encounter?

Some more snakes

A macho culture

Much of the workplace culture in our society (and not just in SET) has been based for many years on a 'standard' and 'male' working pattern: on the supposition that the 'standard' worker will work a 40+ hour week for about 48 weeks a year, for about 40 continuous years, and often for the same organisation.

Does anybody – female *or* male – still do this? Probably not, but the legacy is difficult to shift and it presupposes that the worker can meet all other responsibilities outside traditional working hours.

Some people would argue that SET workplace culture could still be accused of being a 'macho' culture, and as such, one that is 'alien' to women and children. (It is, of course, therefore alien to families and to men too, both directly and indirectly.) While this is possibly no longer true and progress is being made, problems can arise when a woman works in what have been traditionally male areas.

As was discussed in Chapter 1, perhaps one of the most effective ways to change the culture is for more women to enter – and stay in – SET. One of the aims of this book is to assist women to do just that.

Sexual harassment

'Looking back, I realised that there were real problems with my PhD supervisor. I was fairly young then, and didn't know where to turn for advice – I ignored the problems and left. But it is difficult to know what to do when your career is at stake.' Microbiologist

In any career sexual harassment can be a problem, as it relates more to personalities than to particular sectors of business, industry or academia. If you feel you are being sexually harassed, the leaflet *Sexual Harassment – What you can do about it!* published by the Equal Opportunities Commission (see page 113) will give you some guidance on the best way to take effective action.

A long hours culture

One area in particular which militates against women with family responsibilities succeeding in SET, is the fact that SET is acknowledged by most of its participants to be a 'long hours culture'. The long hours culture is yet another feature of modern society. Many people happily work extensive hours and thrive on it. The problem occurs when people are repeatedly judged by the number of hours they are working, rather than by the quality of their work or what they are achieving.

'Even as an undergraduate, my tutors used to view my "extra-curricular activities" with disapproval. It was all right for someone studying the Arts to join the Drama Society – but a scientist? I pointed out that if I had a rehearsal in the evening, it made me get on with setting up my experiments, rather than sitting around drinking cups of coffee with the other students.' Materials scientist

If you enjoy your job, as many scientists and engineers do, working can be a pleasure and might even be preferable to the everyday stresses and strains of family life! Like most satisfying jobs, there are obviously times when 'long hours' and unsociable hours (such as night-time and weekend working) are essential: experiments have to be monitored, projects have to meet deadlines, and conferences have to be attended. However, incessant long hours and overworking on a regular basis can be counter-productive and may eventually have a negative impact on both your personal and your working life as you become less effective – and indeed, less healthy.

'British men have the longest working hours in Europe ... Thirty per cent of sick leave is related to stress, anxiety or depression. Stress at work is costly to business and costly to families.' Janet Walker, The Cost of Communication Breakdown, 1995, page 7

With stress-related illnesses accounting for such a high percentage of absences from work (and some employers have faced demands for compensation as a result of an employee's stress), the business benefits of aiming for a balance between work and leisure time are real. And even in SET, long hours can be shortened, and hours can often be varied: 'I usually go into the lab one or two evenings a week and occasionally at weekends, while my husband looks after our sons. But I am also able to take time off for school assemblies or when the boys are ill, so it works out well.' Research immunologist working in industry

---

Action Plan: Working effectively

If you are being sucked into a long hours culture:

❑ remember being present is not necessarily being productive
❑ resist the myth that you have to work long hours to show commitment – though that might be easier said than done!
❑ expect to be judged on your results, not on the hours you are at work
❑ accept that you need to recharge your batteries.

Then:

❑ delegate as much as possible wherever possible
❑ improve your time management and efficiency and then reduce your hours
❑ resist impossible deadlines
❑ set a limited number of priorities for each day, and aim to meet them
❑ work the hours that are necessary when they are necessary, but expect flexibility on the part of your employer when it comes to meeting *your* needs
❑ refuse to feel guilty and ignore the 'looks' when you go home 'on time': you've finished your work by being more effective. Why haven't they?

'Working practices in the UK are rarely "family friendly". The long hours and macho culture prevalent in most organisations impedes women's progress in two ways: it prevents them from combining career and family themselves and it prevents their partners from taking an active part in the rearing of children. Mothers, fathers and children all suffer.' WNC, Women in the 90s, 1994, page 8

Dual career families

Many women in SET find their career is complicated by the fact that they are part of a 'dual career' family, and one, moreover, where both partners work within similar fields: 'My career has been punctuated by my husband's moves. The Americans call it "the trailing spouse" syndrome. For some time I could not keep my career going as the most obvious options would have meant working under or with my husband. I had to look for alternative solutions. It was hard, but it improved as the children went to school and was worth it in the end.' Research chemist

To run dual careers on 'parallel' lines successfully can be very difficult. It often becomes necessary to designate one career the so-called 'lead' career and act accordingly. However, the 'lead' career can swap from one partner to the other depending on the opportunities and other factors, and this can work well. It is worth reminding yourself of the following encouraging statistic: 'The number of women earning more than their partners has trebled from 1 in 15 in early 1980 to 1 in 5 in 1995.' Helen Wilkinson and Geoff Mulgan, *Freedom's Children: work relationships and politics for 18–34 year olds today*, Demos, 1995

If there is a 'trailing spouse' in your family, remember, it doesn't always have to be *you* all the time. If, however, yours is the lead career (even for the time being) it is important to take full account your partner's personal and career situation while trying to organise your own. And remember, one of the advantages of being a dual career family is that the dual income can provide a better lifestyle and, crucially, better childcare.

How the other half thinks

What is it like being the male partner of a woman who is pursuing a high-flying career in science, engineering or technology? The following profile (in which the names have been changed) gives one man's viewpoint.

We met at university and after we graduated I worked as a chemist in industry and Jennifer as a forensic scientist. Jennifer's work took her to different parts of the country, so we decided to buy a house near my work. We had a 'weekend and mid-week' relationship which wasn't too bad because we didn't have children. Jennifer was then in her mid 20s and she wasn't at all sure about starting a family: her career was important to her. Besides, we both wanted to see the world and pursue our joint passion for rock climbing and so I accepted this, although I was more ready to have children than she was.

Over the next few years Jennifer made several job moves, including one that involved commuting to London, and another that meant us having a 'weekend' relationship as she was working 120 miles away. It wasn't easy, and at times we thought about moving, but as most of the jobs were of limited duration, we decided to stay put.

Six years into our relationship, the enormous benefit of having 'a dual career negotiation rather than a single career commitment' became apparent: with one relatively secure salary I was able to risk going back into university research on a short-term contract. This offered me an exciting but insecure future, but we felt that as a team we had a 'secure-enough' base, and that together we would be all right. I would have felt less comfortable pursuing my career on short-term contracts if Jennifer hadn't been working.

By the time we were in our early 30s, I was very keen to have a family and fortunately Jennifer decided that was what she wanted too. Unfortunately she was now working in London again, commuting four hours a day. That wasn't fun, but the counterbalance was that it was an excellent job and the person she was working with was superb. However, long hours and commuting add up to a lot of stress, too little leisure time and the occasional blazing row, so it wasn't surprising that it was two years before Adam was conceived. Just before Jennifer became pregnant she obtained a new appointment nearer home, and so eventually it all fell into place.

I always knew Jennifer would go back to work, but in fact she found it more difficult than she thought, experiencing 'a horrible turmoil of emotion'. She wanted to spend more time with Adam. Much as I wanted children, I knew that I didn't want to stay at home full-time looking after babies: my research was going very well and I found it both absorbing and challenging. Consequently when Jennifer went back to work, we employed a nanny.

When Jennifer was pregnant with our second child several years later, there was a funding hiatus in the research group where I was working and I started looking for a new job. I obtained a post at another university, and once more we were back to a weekend/mid-week relationship, only now with Jennifer based at home. This time it was more difficult: we were older, both our jobs were more demanding, and, of course, we had two young children. We realised that we did not want to continue on this basis for too long.

Jennifer was again ready for a career move, and after a year managed to get a promotion in London and a house-move was on the cards. We thought about moving to London, but in fact decided to settle nearer my work partly because my hours are more variable – I often go back into the lab at evenings or weekends and at times my research needs very long hours. Jennifer has relatively defined hours and a fairly easy commute (45 minutes, door-to-door). Her job is emotionally demanding, and she actually appreciates the transition time spent between work and home.

I am responsible for the morning and daily childcare. The university has an excellent workplace nursery, and the boys come with me to work and spend the day in the nursery. It's tremendous, and they're fed, watered, entertained and educated. I visit them most lunchtimes, work permitting. I enjoy the extra contact, but it does have the downside that I don't have a clearcut divide between work and home. From the nursery to my desk takes two minutes, and sometimes I find it tricky to stop being a 'hands-on father' and start being a 'researcher'.

Now there's more choices ahead. Adam starts school in September and so do we get another nanny or nanny-share, and take Jack out of the nursery? Or do we leave Jack in the nursery and get a childminder to collect Adam from school?

How does it feel being married to someone who earns twice what I do? Surprisingly, it doesn't bother me, although I would have expected myself to be bothered. But I enjoy the intellectual demands of my work and recognise that the marketplace does not put a high price on university research.

There's a lot of bargaining that goes on in our relationship: what happens if we both have to work late, attend conferences, or when I need to travel abroad, which I have to do at frequent intervals? Like everybody, we have had our share of ups and downs, but I feel Jennifer and I are together in a partnership and I do not think it would have worked for us in any other way. If either of us had stayed at home full-time, we would have gone bananas.

Career patterns in SET

Yet another area where women in SET may encounter particular problems is in the way their careers develop. One career pattern that has become 'classic' for many women in recent years is the following:

- full-time work after completing full-time education
- part-time work (and sometimes lower status, less skilled work) in their late 20s or 30s while or after having children
- full-time work as the children get older.

Some women may also reduce their hours again in middle age if they are the ones who take on caring responsibilities for elderly relatives.

In the past, salary, career progression, conditions of service and pensions did not always take this pattern into account, and many women ended up accepting lower paid, lower status positions than their contemporaries who had worked continuously.

Now, however, increasing numbers of organisations are introducing family-friendly policies (see page 106) which are more in line with contemporary patterns of work.

Other issues

There are several other issues that might – or might not – be relevant to you as a woman working in SET.

- Many careers in SET involve travel away from home, either for work or for conferences, and this again can pose problems.
- Women can be disproportionately affected by the problems of fixed-term contracts (see Chapter 7), and may not have enough flexibility to move readily from post to post.
- Because science and engineering move on so rapidly, even a short absence can mean that an SET professional has become out of date; but too many women are under-confident in this respect and updating oneself is becoming easier (see Chapter 6).
- Taking sabbatical leaves to advance their careers can be difficult for women if these disrupt the family.

- There is a potential clash between what should normally be a researcher's most productive years and the timing of a family.

- Since many women in SET marry 'within the profession' there can be conflicts within dual career families (see page 90) and/or the strain of 'commuting' marriages – as well as the likelihood that their partner is under similar pressures.

'Women scientists and engineers ... have particular problems in that the period when their careers are at a crucial stage often coincides with the years of child-raising. The increasing pace and demands of scientific research and technological development, together with competition for permanent posts, can make it exceptionally difficult to take even a short career break. As more families choose to share caring responsibilities, men as well as women will increasingly face this difficulty.' The Rising Tide, 1994, page 2

So how do you achieve a balance in your life? Can you have it all? Or should you give up trying?

Jane Holland, profiled below, has aimed to achieve a balance in her life and has made a deliberate choice to work less than full-time. For her, branching out early on in her career was the answer, and by taking some decisions before she was quite ready to do so, she has carved out an interesting and challenging career for herself. Joanna Kennedy, profiled on page 115, demonstrates different choices but ones that indicate that you can be both high-powered and highly committed to your family.

Jane Holland, geologist and managing editor of a scientific journal

Jane Holland is in her mid 40s. She has three children, a career she enjoys as managing editor of the Geological Magazine, *and a varied lifestyle.*

After gaining a BA in Geology I worked as a hydrogeologist for three years before moving to Chicago with my husband who was doing a postdoc. I deliberately chose to look for a flexible, lower key job there as I wanted the opportunity to explore and enjoy America. So I literally knocked on doors and found myself a job as editorial assistant on the *Journal of Chemical Physics*. I found editing really suited me – I'm much better at managing and processing than I am at original creative thinking, and I liked the detail of editorial work.

When we moved to Cambridge in the UK I trained as a copy editor at Cambridge University Press (CUP), working on science books ranging from mathematics to earth sciences. I believe I needed my scientific background to do so effectively, because it would have been hard to make the right decisions about the meaning of the text in many instances without some scientific knowledge.

When I had my first baby I started working as a freelance editor because that gave me a huge degree of flexibility. I had intended to stay at home until my children were at school, but when my second daughter was one, the part-time position of managing editor at the *Geological Magazine* came up. Back in America, I'd known someone who worked on the *Journal of Geology* and I'd always thought that would be my ideal job, marrying my skills with the added interest of a familiar subject. Now a comparable job had come up – but three years too soon.

After much heart searching I decided to go for it – it was the only one in Cambridge and it wouldn't come up again – or at least not for years. Happily I got the job and found it did answer all my work requirements. I soon discovered that three mornings at work each week made a wonderful break from two demanding youngsters, much easier than looking after children full-time! My family will always come first, but I do want to be able to combine the priorities of family life without compromising the integrity of work.

Over the last ten years, I have actively developed my editorial role, as well as having a third baby and taking a sabbatical year in Australia with my family: on both occasions I arranged cover for the career break myself. I've developed the systems of the journal – it's mostly on computer and I've just been connected to email. I've also expanded the book review section. The academic editors now delegate a great deal of responsibility to me, and I work very independently.

I work in the Department of Earth Sciences at the university, which is a congenial place to work – geologists are friendly sorts! I appreciate being able to read around the research in the field and like the flexibility and variety of my work – there's never too much of any one thing and I can chop and change. At times I've become overloaded – deadlines are critical – but I've structured things so that I can still work part-time, that is, during school hours. For instance, when things became busier with the increased turnover of manuscripts, I delegated the straightforward copy-editing to a freelancer.

God has been good in giving me a job that balances well with the more important things of life.

Achieving a balance

When trying to balance your work and your home life, there are many issues that can arise, and no simple advice that can help you to solve the problem, and no single right answer.

Some women are lucky and have a supportive partner and family; other women are not so fortunate. A mentor (see Chapter 4) who has experienced and dealt with similar problems and pressures can help you to achieve a balance. The point to bear in mind is, that whatever your own particular situation, you *can* make the most of it.

Many of the women who are most at ease with the different parts of their lives have developed the habit of discussing the tough issues and creating a shared agenda with the people whose lives impact on their own – and this is no easy task. The day-today running of a busy life often leaves insufficient time to talk through the implications of the current scenario with your nearest and dearest, but it is vitally important to carve out the space to discuss shared values and joint enterprises such as childrearing, financial underpinning and home and leisure priorities.

Finding the right questions, and then asking them, and then really listening to the answers, sounds like nothing more than common sense. It is. But all too often it is common sense that is not so common.

Once you start asking the questions that really matter, you can begin to work towards some of the solutions.

Tackling some of the issues

We've known for centuries that 'all work and no play' can make for a dull life, but achieving that elusive balance can be a difficult task at many different stages of our lives, whether we are married or single, and whether or not we have children. For many women, though, family issues are perhaps the most difficult and so these are the issues on which the rest of this chapter concentrates.

Timing a family

'I've told employers so often I'm not going to have children I'm starting to believe it.'
Young mechanical engineer

If you want a family – and these days we are allowed to say 'if' as increasing numbers of people are choosing to remain childfree – when do you and your partner start thinking about having a baby? Is there ever a 'right' time? Before you're established or later on? One scientist felt: 'I wanted an adventure before I committed myself to the responsibility of a family. I'd been bitten by the Antarctic bug at 19 but I was 27 before I went. I spent five months there studying epiphytic algal assemblages in the maritime Antarctic. I was the first woman to work on the base. I had the time of my life.' Research oceanographer

On the other hand, if you want children and yet keep postponing the decision, you might have problems: 'They're 43 when they start thinking about wanting a baby ... and they're 46 when they accept it isn't going to happen ... deliberately delaying childbirth is a relatively new phenomenon ... in fact the ideal time is between 28 and 35.' Gail Sheehy, *New Passages*, HarperCollins Publishers Ltd, 1996, pages 106-107

Unfortunately the years between 28 and 35 are precisely the time when you need to put energy into your career if you wish to succeed. Although assisted fertility techniques are reducing this problem, declining fertility as you get older might be something you and your partner wish to bear in mind.

Another consideration might be your current work situation: it is important to consider your employer, managers and colleagues – is this a good time? How would you feel in their position (which might be *your* position at a future stage in your career)? Taking maternity leave soon after starting a new job or at a critical stage in a project should normally be avoided.

However, other women have managed to have a family and a career, as the profiles throughout this book indicate. You can do both too.

- 'I had my children early on and then returned to research later through a returners' scheme.' Research biologist
- 'Combining a career and taking professional exams and having children can be a nightmare. But we survived.' Electronic engineer
- 'I used the time when the children were little to finish writing up my PhD and publish some papers. The minute they fell asleep or went to playgroup I ignored the breakfast dishes and attacked the word processor. Having only a limited amount of time certainly makes you quit procrastinating.' Research chemist
- 'Sometimes it's easy to forget starting a family should be a joint decision with your partner. We talked it through together and timed our first baby to coincide with a sabbatical abroad. By the time we got back, I was ready to start work again.' Physicist

A few women get it impossibly right:

'We planned both our children to be born at the start of the long summer vacation and to our amazement it worked out ... '

Well, almost right.

' ... except that our daughter arrived a day early and so I missed an examiners' meeting.' Research zoologist

Whatever your decision, the keys to successfully combining a career and starting a family seem to be:

- get informed
- work through all the issues with your partner and make sure that you understand each other (not always as simple as it sounds) and are in agreement
- and get mentally and physically prepared.

Chapter 6 on women returners offers guidance on how best to plan for and minimise the impact of a career break.

If you decide to have children, it is important to check out your position at work and your maternity rights. The following checklist indicates the situation with regard to maternity rights at the time of writing, but as this is liable to change from time to time, please confirm all details with your local Benefits Agency.

Checklist: Your maternity rights

As a working mother-to-be, you are the beneficiary of certain legal rights to protect your health and job, and will usually be entitled to some financial help when you give up work to have your baby. Some of these rights apply to all pregnant women who do paid work; for others, there are qualifying conditions.

Time off for antenatal care

Are you eligible?
Yes – all pregnant women, whatever the hours they work or however long they have been in their job, are entitled not to be unreasonably refused paid time off work for antenatal care.

What do you get?
Paid time off for visits to the hospital, your GP and other antenatal appointments. This might include antenatal classes if your GP, midwife or health visitor confirms in writing that these are part of your antenatal care.

Maternity Leave of 14 weeks'

Are you eligible?
Yes – all women are entitled to 14 weeks' Maternity Leave, no matter how long they have worked for an employer, if they are in work while they are pregnant. It doesn't matter whether the work is full or part-time. However you do not have an automatic right to be paid during this leave (consult the following sections on Statutory Maternity Pay and Maternity Allowance).

What do you get?
Fourteen weeks' leave and the right to go back to an equivalent job in the same organisation. During the period of leave, the terms and conditions of your employment (*except* for pay) must be maintained. This includes pension contributions, holiday entitlement and perks such as company cars.

Maternity Absence

Are you eligible?
If you have worked continuously for the same employer for two years by the beginning of the 11th week before your baby is due, then you are entitled to Maternity Absence. The exception to this is if your employer employs five or fewer people.

What do you get?
The Maternity Absence period runs from the end of your 14 weeks' Maternity Leave until the end of the 28th week after your baby is born.

Statutory Maternity Pay (SMP)

Are you eligible?
You must have worked for the same employer for at least 26 weeks by the end of the qualifying week (the 15th week before the week in which your baby is due) *and* you must still be in your job in this 15th week *and* you must be earning a specified amount a week or more on average.

What do you get?
SMP is paid weekly for up to 18 weeks. Even if you do not plan to return to your job you can still get it, and if you decide not to go back to work you won't have to repay it.

For the first six weeks you are entitled to 90% of your average weekly earnings. After that you get the basic rate of SMP for up to 12 weeks. (You will not get SMP for any weeks when you work.)

Maternity Allowance (MA)

Are you eligible?
If you can't get SMP – for instance if you are self-employed, or if you stopped working or changed jobs during your pregnancy – you might be entitled to this weekly allowance.

You must have worked and paid full-rate national insurance contributions for at least 26 of the 66 weeks before the week in which your baby is expected.

What do you get?
Maternity Allowance is paid for up to 18 weeks. Like SMP, you can choose when to start your MA. The amount you receive will vary depending on whether you are self-employed, unemployed, or employed, but you will only receive it for weeks in which you aren't working.

Other rights

Your employer cannot dismiss you or make you redundant in preference to comparable employees for *any* reason connected with your pregnancy or maternity leave.

If you are pregnant, have had a baby within the previous six months, or are breastfeeding, your employer must make certain that the work you are doing does not endanger your baby's health.

What else is available?

Other benefits which you might be eligible for include Incapacity Benefit, Maternity Payments from the Social Fund, and health benefits. Once your baby is born, there are Child Benefits, One Parent Benefit, Family Credit and so on.

In every case, you should check what you need to do to qualify for the above benefits. Further information and leaflets can be obtained from either your local Benefits Agency, your nearest citizens' advice bureau or the Maternity Alliance (see page 117).

Childcare choices

If you're feeling guilty about being a working mother, you're not alone: more and more women with children are working longer hours and having to deal with the conficting demands upon their time and their emotions.

'In 1973, 43 per cent of couples with dependent children were both working outside the home: by 1992 this had risen to 60 per cent.' Janet Walker, The Cost of Communication Breakdown, 1995, page 7

You might not stop feeling guilty, but you can ease your conscience if you have effective childcare arrangements. Good childcare is critical if you are going to be able to concentrate on work while you are at work. You might think first of a mixture of friends and family, and this can be successful. But as your career becomes more demanding, you will probably find you will have to become more business-like in your approach to childcare, although you may want to have fallback arrangements with family and friends: 'Be as professional about your childcare arrangements as you are about your job. Be prepared to pay. Always have contingency plans, and be prepared to invest money (and time) in a support network which hopefully will include a cleaner as well.' Civil engineer

There are many good books and articles which discuss childcare options in some detail. Several are listed on page 119. This section does not aim to analyse the options in depth, but raises some of the points you will need to consider.

Childcare for younger children

What are the options?

- partner, friends or relatives
- nannies
- au pairs
- childminders
- nurseries

Against each of these options, you might like to consider the following decision-making factors for your particular situation:

- the needs of your child
- quality of the carer's relationship with children
- convenience
- availability
- stability
- flexibility
- stress factors

- cost
- you/your partner's expectations (about the job/about the way you want your child to be looked after)
- the carer's expectations (about the job/about the way they will be allowed to look after the child)
- a viable option?

For example, if your partner or mother is prepared to look after the children, will this be the 'ideal' option or could it be untenable and cause other personal and social problems? You might find you end up paying a high emotional 'price' for a 'cheaper' option, and decide that a formal paid arrangement might be more effective.

Live-in help versus live-out

Perhaps the first decision you need to make is whether you want live-in or live-out help. You might not have much choice: 'I am a single parent and I knew I would be travelling abroad to visit the plant in Germany at least a couple of times a month. I had no choice: I had to have live-in help, which meant an au pair or a nanny.' Chemical engineer

Advantages of live-in helps
- Your child is cared for in her or his own home.
- You do not have to take or collect your child before or after work and so you won't have the struggle to get them dressed first thing in the morning!
- Live-in helpers can cover for you over unsociable or long hours.
- You should not have a problem during holidays, or if your child is sick.
- You might find you get some domestic help – such as cooking or light housework (although with a nanny this will only be with regard to the child) – as well.

Disadvantages of live-in helps
- You and your family may lack privacy in your own home, and you may never 'get the house to yourself'.
- You may lack space.
- If your help is ill or unhappy, you may have to look after and/or support them.
- You may become jealous of their closeness with your child.
- Your house might 'suffer' from increased wear and tear, the live-in help's friends and loud music.

Successful live-in help often depends on a detailed and precise definition of what the job involves and its conditions – you will have to think about working hours, care of children's rooms and clothes, eating and laundry arrangements, holidays. Then you will have to consider what your policy will be on smoking, boyfriends or girlfriends, the phone, discipline, access to the car and so on.

It is essential to draw up a written contract so that all parties are clear about such matters.

Nannies

A nanny is usually professionally trained and with a recognised childcare qualification. A nanny will look after your children in their own home, and may either live in or come in on a daily basis. It is advisable to recruit your nanny from a reputable agency, and to check all references thoroughly, and ask the agency for proof of her working record. Nannies are not registered with or insured by the local authority.

Advantages of nannies
- Nannies can offer a personal childcare service tailored to your child's and your family's needs.
- Nannies are usually trained and/or experienced professional carers of children.
- They will usually have chosen childcare as a profession and should therefore enjoy their job!
- They should be able to take and collect your child from school and other activities.
- There can be built-in flexibility with a nanny, for instance if you work variable hours or need to be away overnight.
- Your child will have a stable one-to-one relationship with their carer, usually for a lengthy period.

Disadvantages of nannies
- This may be an expensive option unless you have more than one child, although you might be able to do a 'nanny share' which can reduce the costs.
- There may be a lack of family privacy.
- You will have to deal with tax, national insurance contributions and other employment matters although some agencies might do this for you.
- You may find that you have a high 'turnover' rate of nannies.

Au pairs

An au pair is another form of live-in help. An au pair is usually a young, unmarried foreigner of between 17 and 27 years in age who wants to learn English and live as a member of your family, often for about a year. They usually work for five hours per day in return for accommodation in their own room, two full days off a week, and a small allowance.

Advantages of au pairs

- Au pairs will have similar advantages to nannies, but they are usually a less expensive choice and can prove to be very good value.

- Au pairs might be particularly suitable with slightly older children, and sometimes fulfil the role of an older brother or sister.

- Your children will meet people from other cultures and countries, and will often learn about 'social adaptability'.

- You could choose a male au pair if you want to introduce a more 'masculine' ingredient into your children's early childcare.

- Babysitting is usually an agreed part of au pair's job, so you will have a readily available babysitter, and you will not have to rush home the moment you've gulped down the after-dinner coffee.

- Your children might pick up some foreign languages.

Disadvantages of au pairs

- Au pairs can be homesick – or lovesick!

- You, and more importantly your children, may have communication problems – your au pair's English might be poor. If this is the case, your children's development may not be stretched or stimulated by their company.

- They can lack experience of children, cooking and housework.

- They do not usually have any professional childcare training and you might not want to entrust a young baby to them.

- You might find you have acquired an extra 'child'.

- Au pairs are usually in their teens, and they might have some of the disadvantages of a normal teenager such as moodiness, self-centredness, noisy friends and insensitivity.

- You may have a high turnover of au pairs, and you will certainly have to 'train' a new au pair at least once a year.

Childminders

Childminders look after children in the childminder's own home for payment. By law, childminders who look after children under five years of age have to be registered with the local authority. This involves a health and safety check. Childminders are often mothers with children of their own.

Advantages of childminders

- With a careful initial selection, childminders can prove a good long-term option. (Always check that your childminder is registered with the local authority.)

- A good childminder will have experience of and enjoy working with children.

- The child will be cared for in a 'home atmosphere', and might have a daily routine which involves local activities and networks, shopping, picking up other children from school and 'everyday' events that they might experience if you were not working.
- Childminding can be a flexible and relatively economical method of caring.
- Your child will have other children for company, which is an important part of their development.

Disadvantages of childminders

- Good childminders are sometimes in short supply.
- They may only be able to offer limited hours.
- If your child or the childminder is ill, you will have a problem.
- Your child might not get on with the other children, or may pick up ailments from them.
- You will probably have to take your child to the childminder's home and collect him or her at an appointed time.

Nurseries

In a nursery, your child will be cared for with other children. There are many different types of nurseries including those run by employers, local councils, charities, communities and private businesses. Day nurseries have to be registered by the local authority and should be inspected annually.

Advantages of nurseries

- A good nursery is child-centred and child-friendly.
- Your child is mixing with other children in a safe and stimulating environment.
- You are not dependent on a single person and so are not vulnerable if that person is ill or decides to stop caring for your child.
- Nurseries can help a child make a smooth transition to school and its routines.
- Some nurseries are open the whole year round.

Disadvantages of nurseries

- Your child (and you) might have to spend time travelling to and from the nursery every day.
- Nurseries will not usually look after sick children.
- There may be a lack of one-to-one attention.
- You may not like the fact that your child is being cared for in an 'institutional' setting.
- There may be a lack of flexibility with regard to hours and holidays.
- Nurseries can be expensive.

Many families discover that they mix and match their childcare arrangements, according to the specific factors operating at any one time such as the age and situation of their children, the careers involved, and the money available. Talking to your friends and mentors who have been down similar paths is a useful way of exploring what might work best for you.

Childcare for older children

Once your children are of school age, you have a whole new set of problems. Then you may have to start investigating 'out-of-school care': pre and after school care, playschemes, and holiday arrangements.

Even when your children become teenagers, you will need to ensure that they are being supervised or at least have someone to turn to, even though they might resist it. Many parents would argue that the help that you could most usefully employ at this stage might be a chauffeur!

If you are beginning to get a sinking feeling, remember that having work you enjoy (and an income!) will benefit your children in many ways, and you can always take heart from research like the following:

'Children viewed a working parent very positively and often benefitted from high-quality childcare. For example, they enjoyed going to the out-of-school club rather than being at home on their own with a parent.' Women's National Commission, The Workplace Culture: long hours, high stress, page 11

Elder and dependant care

Like many other people, you may find that elder and/or dependant care will become another area of your life which you need to manage.

'Nearly 7 million people in the UK are carers. In other words, one in seven adults looks after a relative or friend who cannot manage without help because of sickness, age or disability.
About 3.9 million carers are women and 2.9 million are men.'
Carers National Association leaflet, 1997

Once again, you will need to work your way through the issues, such as:

- do you arrange care for your elderly relatives in their own home?
- or in your home?
- or in a residential home?

And you will need to weigh up the options that are available and possible, such as:

- day centre care

- respite care
- private home helps
- local authority home helps
- meals on wheels
- community nursing
- private nurses
- suitable residential homes
- disability aids
- allowances available.

Elder care is an issue that is not going to go away, and many organisations now allow for such commitments in their employment policies.

Family-friendly policies

Whatever your responsibilities, there are no easy solutions, but there *are* solutions. One area where progress is being made is the expansion of 'family-friendly policies' that more enlightened employers are promoting for both women and men. When you are considering working for an organisation, you might see how far their employment policies meet the criteria in the following checklist. However, if you are still at an early stage in the 'job negotiation process', it might be wisest to 'get your feet under the desk first', and then start negotiating for improved policies.

Checklist: Employment policies – best practice

In an ideal world, you would hope to be offered the following features by an employer:

❑ a formal equal opportunity policy statement (which covers race, gender and disability) issued by the employer which is regularly monitored for its effectiveness, and for the evaluation of and review of targets.

Maternity and paternity rights

❑ enhanced maternity and paternity rights
❑ maternity, paternity and adoption leave, and making that leave allowable as pension time

Career breaks

❑ career breaks or family leave not just for having children, but also for eldercare, for looking after ill members of the family, or for other pressing family or educational and training needs
❑ keeping-in-touch schemes during a career break

Hours of work

Flexible working arrangements such as:

- ❑ phased in part-time work after maternity/paternity/adoption leave, without loss of status or rights
- ❑ flexitime (which enables you to vary your hours around a fixed core time)
- ❑ annual hours contracts (working a certain number of hours/days/weeks over a year)
- ❑ voluntary reduced work hours or V-time working (employees can cut their hours by an agreed amount, and work either a shorter working day, a shorter working week or take extra holiday)
- ❑ job sharing (two people share the responsibilities and benefits of one permanent full-time job)
- ❑ term-time working (perhaps with the salary spread equally over the year)
- ❑ compressed hours (more hours each day, but fewer days a week or month)
- ❑ telecommuting and/or the opportunity to work from home (which is becoming far more feasible with the advent of new technology, and, when it is an integral part of company policy, can offer employers lower costs and higher productivity)
- ❑ the provision of similar employment benefits for part-time employees as for full-time employees

Childcare facilities

- ❑ childcare support (e.g. workplace nurseries)
- ❑ holiday playschemes
- ❑ parent support network
- ❑ time off when children are sick

Research policies

- ❑ part-time research fellowships
- ❑ portable research awards/fellowships which allow mobility, maternity and paternity leave, and remove residential qualifications
- ❑ fellowships for returners incorporating a period of refresher training

(See also Chapter 6 on women returners, and the section on individual Research Councils' policies on page 109.)

Health and personal development policies

- ❑ lifestyle screening and confidential counselling (career, health, personal and stress advice and counselling)
- ❑ open learning and other training facilities which bear equal opportunities in mind
- ❑ various forms of support if you move with your job.

NOTE: All family-friendly policies should be available to men as well as women. This is not only fair – it is a requirement of the Sex Discrimination legislation.

If you are thinking of working for an organisation, you might want to check out whether it has:

- an equal opportunity policy statement, and if so, how does it monitor its effectiveness and evaluate the outcomes?
- action plans for internal and external strategic development and improvement
- female role models in high positions
- women on the board
- a commitment to and involvement in initiatives such as Opportunity 2000 (see below).

Opportunity 2000

Opportunity 2000 is a business-led and government-endorsed initiative aimed at increasing 'the quality and quantity of women's participation in the workforce'. Opportunity 2000 aims to demonstrate that by effectively capitalising on the skills and talents of the female workforce, for example by instituting family-friendly policies and – most importantly – by monitoring subsequent progress, employers increase their competitive capability and reap commercial benefits. By 1997 Opportunity 2000 had over 300 member organisations which collectively employed over 25% of the UK workforce. Find out more from:

Opportunity 2000
Business in the Community
44 Baker Street
London
W1M 1DH
Tel: 0171 224 1600; fax: 0171 486 1700

Trades unions

Various trades unions are keen to promote both family-friendly policies and the increased participation of women in the SET workforce. You can find out more about the union that is most relevant to you from the Trades Union Congress (TUC) whose address is on page 211.

In general, career breaks and good family-friendly policies make sound business sense. Employers instituting them often find they swiftly recoup any investment they make as they start to see benefits in the form of decreased recruitment and training costs, and increased employee commitment and productivity.

'At GCHQ (Government Communications Headquarters), for example, it has been calculated that it costs £1,100 to recruit a graduate, and about £92,000 to train a graduate trainee project manager in the unique demands of this business. When GCHQ recently introduced flexible working patterns and allowed four women scientists to work flexibly following maternity leave, the organisation reckons to have saved some £400,000 by retaining these four talented and experienced people.' Opportunity 2000, Tapping the Talent, 1997, page 7

Family-friendly and equal opportunity policies are gaining ground. The Research Councils, for example, now have a variety of initiatives, as the following summary demonstrates.

Research Councils' employment policies

Biotechnology and Biological Sciences Research Council (BBSRC)

- user friendly guide to maternity and childcare for BBSRC employees, containing information about maternity rights and opportunities for flexible working, including:
  - flexible maternity and paternity leave
  - career breaks
  - keeping-in-touch schemes
  - adoption and dependency care leave
  - childcare provision at several BBSRC workplace nurseries
  - holiday playschemes on several sites
  - after-school care scheme on one site
  - job sharing, term-time working, homeworking, part-time working
- equal opportunity awareness seminars
- identification and active promotion of female role models and flexible working patterns
- member of Opportunity 2000 and Parents at Work (see page 118)
- progress on equal opportunity policies featured in annual reports

Council for the Central Laboratory of the Research Councils (CCLRC)

- career breaks
- flexible working hours are a possibility
- some nursery care facilities and holiday play schemes in operation
- possibility of unpaid leave in the school holidays
- access to welfare facilities providing support and an independent confidential counselling and advisory service
- 'Balancing work and home' courses, which provide advice and support, and out of which a Working Parents' Network has evolved
- policies on harassment and bullying, backed up by support mechanisms of trained counsellors and welfare officers
- progress on equal opportunity policies featured in annual report

Engineering and Physical Sciences Research Council (EPSRC)

- a range of family-friendly policies including:
  - career breaks of up to five years
  - flexible working hours
  - part-time working
  - job sharing
  - homeworking (subject to job requirements)
- access to a workplace nursery
- maternity pay provision extended from 14 weeks to 18 weeks' full pay
- progress on equal opportunity policies featured in annual reports

Medical Research Council (MRC)

- career breaks
- part-time work possible, including job sharing and homeworking where feasible
- access to workplace nurseries at some of the larger sites
- equal opportunities training and monitoring
- childcare support on some training courses
- harassment policies in place, supported by trained staff
- member of Opportunity 2000
- funding a longitudinal comparative research study of factors affecting the career commitment of male and female research scientists

- MRC's National Equal Opportunities Subcommittee determines priorities and monitors progress, and has published a Guide and Action Statement for the use of MRC staff
- MRC is currently considering a programme of action intended to lead over time to reducing the wastage rate among women embarking on careers in medical research

Natural Environment Research Council (NERC)

- family-friendly policies include:
  - career breaks of up to five years
  - part-time working
  - flexitime working
  - annual hours contract
  - homeworking arrangements
- progress on assistance with childcare at some workplace nurseries and local private nurseries, and also formulating a childcare voucher policy for other sites
- maternity pay provision extended from 14 weeks to 18 weeks' full pay
- equal opportunities awareness and training is an integral part of NERC management training
- women's groups have been established at some sites
- progress to be published in annual report

Particle Physics and Astronomy Research Council (PPARC)

- has followed best practice over the years in offering:
  - career breaks
  - special leave for domestic reasons
  - maternity and paternity leave
  - part-time working
  - job sharing
  - flexible working hours
  - nursery provision and holiday play schemes
  - non-residential training courses
- statements and guidelines issued to staff on equal opportunities, preventing and remedying all forms of harassment, and preventing age discrimination
- part-time staff and fixed-term appointees are classed as non-mobile; in other grades, in practice staff are only transferred with their agreement

- corporate plan includes fair employment as a performance measure to monitor employment practice, and consideration is being given to the inclusion of a summary of progress in future annual reports

---

Other organisations such as The Wellcome Trust support family-friendly policies too. See, for example, page 134 which gives details of The Wellcome Trust's Re-entry Fellowship Scheme.

Fiona Cox, senior personnel adviser, Pfizer Central Research

Fiona Cox outlines some of the family-friendly policies that Pfizer offers its staff.

In the pharmaceutical industry everything moves so fast that it is generally difficult to make extended career breaks work. Our philosophy is to offer enhanced maternity benefits, flexible working such as job sharing, homeworking opportunities, and extensive childcare support to enable parents who have children to combine work with raising their family. For example, we support a part-time phased return to work, or, if possible, a package where men and women could work two days a week at home and three in the office. Obviously this is not possible in all jobs, but it works very well, for example in the positions which involve report writing, and those working in statistics and allied professions.

One of the programmes we are particularly proud of is the fact that we offer childcare support for the full 0–14 age range: when a child starts school is often the time when the childcare problems really begin. We have developed the Pfizer Child Care Support Service together with an external organisation. They provide our employees with pre- and post-natal childcare support, run our holiday playscheme and other out-of-school activities.

I couldn't tell you how many *women* take advantage of our 'family-friendly' policies because they are aimed at our *employees*, not women specifically. This is about families, and we aim to have a *family*-friendly culture.

Health

All your careful planning, all your intricately organised childcare arrangements and all your years of training and working can be shattered overnight if you do not look after yourself as well as your family. For many women this is easier said than done, and with some justification you might cry 'but how do I find the time?' There's a tough answer to that question: if you don't find the time to stay healthy, you might be forced to 'find' that time to be ill.

To cope, you need to maintain good levels of health and energy; you won't if you don't. There is a plethora of information available in books, magazines and information leaflets, about diet and exercise, so unfortunately you really don't have any excuse ...

Equal Opportunities Commission (EOC)

The EOC publishes a range of up-to-date information on issues such as maternity rights, family-friendly policies and job sharing. Much of this information is aimed at employers as well as employees, and lists the benefits of adopting certain practices – as well as the legal implications of not doing so in certain cases. It also runs nctworks where local employers can exchange information on good practice. Contact:

The Employment Policy Unit
The Equal Opportunities Commission
Overseas House
Quay Street
Manchester
M3 3HN
Tel: 0161 833 9244; fax: 0161 835 1657

Strategies for success

How have other women in similar positions managed to cope?

Here are some strategies that have helped them, and that might help you.

- Try setting deliberate boundaries between your work and home life.

  'I make a point of not thinking about work issues at home, or about home issues at work. It's a bit artificial, and it doesn't always work, but at least it's something to aim for.' Quality engineer

- Don't take work home.

  'It's important to have a clear division of time or the children can be all too easily neglected. I work a lot on site and only bring work home in an emergency: the evenings, weekends and our holidays are for me and the children.' Civil engineer

- Be resourceful.

  'As my children became teenagers surprisingly they seemed to need me around more, especially during their exam years. This was one reason why I started my own IT consultancy.' IT consultant

- Minimise the stresses and strains.

  'When I was single, I loved travelling but now I only travel when I really have to. With phones, faxes and email, you don't always need to make that trip.' Telecommunications consultant

- Make time for yourself.

  'I found that with my commitment to my research and my commitment to my family, there was no time for me. Now I go early morning swimming twice a week on my way to the lab. It's time just for me and it keeps me fit.' Research microbiologist

- Recognise your own limits.

  'I try to start early and leave promptly at 5 o'clock. I recognise the danger signs now when I'm trying to do too much and aim to stop myself. Sometimes I stop earlier than I would have done when I didn't have a family. Otherwise I just end up yelling at the kids.' Industrial chemist

- Be realistic.

  'You can't do as much as you want to, so don't get overloaded. I've learned to say "no" to impossible deadlines and expect my family to help out at home. But I'm still the one who cleans the loos.' Customer focus manager

- Choose a life – not a lifestyle.

  'Lots of women in our lab are trying to keep a career going at full speed and run a family. The marriage usually ends up as a casualty. You have to continually assess what's really important to you. It's about compromise and balance. The most important achievement in my life, and one that I have to continue to strive for, is to achieve a balance of home and work, career and family.' Geologist

- Have fun!

  'We realised we were planning our life so carefully, we had lost the spontaneity. Fun can be the glue that holds families together.' Mechanical engineer

Whether you have a supportive partner, or an unsupportive partner or no partner; whether you have one child or three or six; whether you work in the lab or in the field or out on the ocean, balancing an interesting career and a family life is always difficult.

But you *can* do it.

Joanna Kennedy, OBE, FEng, chartered civil engineer and project manager

Joanna Kennedy is a civil engineer in her mid 40s. She combines her demanding role as mother of two energetic sons, aged nine and eleven, with the equally demanding role of director of Ove Arup & Partners.

When I left school with A-levels in mathematics and physics, I wanted to do something useful which would combine my technical and creative skills. Civil engineering attracted me: I felt it would give me the opportunity to design and build structures that were beautiful, but could I be successful in a male-dominated field? One firm I visited before university told me bluntly that they would never employ a female engineer – 'because she wouldn't cope with the bad language and muddy boots on site'.

When I graduated in the early 1970s it was very gratifying to be offered a job by that same firm. I turned it down to work with Ove Arup as a design engineer and I've been with them ever since. I didn't feel the need to move elsewhere because Ove Arup constantly provides me with new challenges and opportunities. It's an enjoyable place to work and I like the company ethos which marries high quality projects with a respect for the environment, opportunities for the individual, and a firm commitment to its staff as its main asset.

Good family-friendly policies have been another reason for my staying put. I've had two career breaks; after each of them I came back part-time at first, and I managed to demonstrate that you could be part-time *and* hold down a responsible position. I think the career breaks did set me back initially with regard to promotion, but I've now 'caught up' again. Ove Arup recognises what you can do as a person – not whether you are male or female. You are accepted for what you can contribute. Now I work full-time but I've negotiated an agreement where I can take a certain amount of additional unpaid leave during the school holidays, project responsibilities permitting. This is possible even at the level at which I work.

I've had a lot of support and encouragement from my firm and my family, even though my husband also has a demanding job. Flexibility on all sides is the key: I've got a good team I can delegate to and I make it clear that I'm always contactable by telephone and fax. At times I work long hours so I have always had full-time childcare, but at others I work from home or will take time off for family reasons such as to watch my sons' football team. I believe people should be judged on what they achieve – what they do and how they do it – and not the hours they work.

For me, each new project is a challenge and an opportunity. Perhaps my favourite early achievement is the Runnymede Bridge over the M25. I worked on the construction site for two years and it was very exciting seeing something I had designed actually built. In my early years with Ove Arup I designed and built bridges and other infrastructures. During the last eight years I have led and managed multi-disciplinary teams on a range of building and civil engineering projects. Project management is like a complex jigsaw: the team has to pull together to meet the client's requirements within the financial and time constraints, to facilitate the design process, and to make sure the project works.

At the moment I'm Project Director of the £150 million South Bank Arts centre redevelopment in London. That's been a fascinating new experience as I had to learn about the Lottery Assessment Process and really had to understand what the various arts organisations want and need. Once you appreciate the client's vision and objectives, you have to work out how you can realise them in terms of a design brief, an architectural response, a business plan and a funding strategy.

I think women can and do succeed. There are tremendous opportunities around and women should 'give it a go'. It doesn't matter if you make a mistake. You've got to challenge the conventional wisdom and be prepared to make things work for you: life can be more flexible than you expect. At times I've had to make the running: I helped to institute a career break scheme at Ove Arup for example.

Don't be afraid to define your priorities and then stick to them, whether they're taking your children to the dentist or building an underground station. Refuse to accept people's perception of what you can and can't do. Take the bad language and the muddy boots, for example. There has never been a problem: when I'm on site the language is modified and I rather enjoy getting my boots muddy.

Further information

The following list of organisations is not exhaustive, but indicates the range of groups that are providing information and support on questions such as balancing work and home, and campaigning for better conditions and policies.

Carers National Association

A support and campaigning organisation, which provides information and a wide range of written materials, some in minority languages, and aims to raise awareness of carer issues.

Carers National Association
20–25 Glasshouse Yard
London EC1A 4JS
Tel: 0171 490 8818 (CarersLine: 0345 573 369 1–4pm weekdays);
fax: 0171 490 8824

Kids' Club Network

This network promotes and supports out-of-school care for school-age children.

Kids' Club Network
Bellerive House
3 Muirfield Crescent
London E14 9SZ
Tel: 0171 512 2100; fax: 0171 512 2010

Maternity Alliance

Through a programme of campaigns, information, research and training, the Maternity Alliance aims to improve health and social policy in the area of maternity care. It also publishes clear and up-to-date leaflets about rights and services for mothers, fathers and babies.

Maternity Alliance
45 Beech Street
London EC2P 2LX
Tel: 0171 588 8582; fax: 0171 588 8584

National Childbirth Trust

The NCT is a great way of getting to know other parents and parents-to-be, including working mothers. It provides local ante- and postnatal classes throughout the country, support and information in pregnancy, childbirth and early parenthood, and aims to enable every parent to make informed choices. It has an extensive range of information resources.

National Childbirth Trust
Alexandra House
Oldham Terrace
Acton
London W3 6NH
Tel: 0181 992 8637; fax: 0181 992 5929

National Council for One Parent Families

This provides free information to lone parents on a wide variety of issues including returning to work and childcare options.

National Council for One Parent Families
255 Kentish Town Road
London NW5 2LX
Tel: 0171 267 1361; fax: 0171 482 4851

New Ways to Work

New Ways to Work was founded to campaign for changes in the culture of the workplace so that people could have some choice about the number and arrangement of hours they worked in paid employment. The organisation promotes flexible working hours, term-time working, job sharing and career breaks.

New Ways to Work
309 Upper Street
London N1 2TY
Tel: 0171 226 4026; fax: 0171 354 2978; email: nww@dircon.co.uk

Parents at Work

A national network which is committed to the welfare of children with working parents, Parents at Work offers support and information nationally and through local groups where parents can talk about the problems of combining work and childcare. The organisation also advises employers and campaigns for better conditions. It publishes a series of information leaflets and books on childcare options, flexible working and returning to work.

Parents at Work
45 Beech Street
London
EC2Y 8AD
Tel: 0171 628 3578 (helpline); fax: 0171 628 3591

Background reading

Women in the 90s

Written, published by and obtainable from the Women's National Commission (WNC – see page 198), 1994

Interesting and informative background reading on the specific problems women face in the 1990s, and what can be done to overcome some of the obstacles. There are chapters on lone-parent families, women returners and older women.

Workplace Culture – long hours, high stress?

Written, published by and obtainable from the WNC (see page 198), 1995

A short report on a seminar arranged by the WNC in December 1995, and includes the views of Sir Nicholas Goodison, chair of the TSB Group, and representatives of the Labour Research Department, New Ways to Work, and Parents at Work.

The Working Woman's Handbook

Polly Bird, Piatkus, 1996

An easy if sometimes general read covering a range of topics. There are useful chapters on equal opportunities, women's finances, childcare choices, health and safety and sexual harassment, a comprehensive list of addresses and a good reading list.

Sexual harassment

Sexual harassment - what you can do about it!

Equal Opportunities Commission, 1994

An informative booklet, obtainable from the Equal Opportunities Commission (EOC) (see page 113).

Maternity and health issues

Maternity Rights: a guide for employers and employees PL958 (REV1)

Department of Trade and Industry and the Health & Safety Executive, 1995

Factual information for employees and employers on your rights during pregnancy, during your absence from work, and once you return to your job. Includes qualifying conditions, what you get and what you need to do. There is a useful chapter on health and safety.

There are many good books on pregnancy and childcare, and women's health issues: take a look in your local bookshop or library to find one that appeals to you. You might enjoy the following titles which include real-life case histories.

Becoming a Family

Anna McGrail, NCT Publishing, 1996

This book looks at what being a parent is really like, how to cope with the practicalities of babycare, and how to manage the emotional and sexual changes that parenthood brings.

Work & Home: finding the balance

Teresa Wilson, NCT Publishing, 1996

Work & Home offers solutions provided by other parents to the challenges of managing the demands of home and work, and ways in which you can deal with changing priorities and the problems of organising childcare.

The New Our Bodies Ourselves

The Boston Women's Health Book Collective, British edition by Angela Phillips and Jill Rakusen, Penguin Books, revised edition 1996

Subtitled 'a health book by and for women', this 'classic', was first published in 1971 and has been regularly updated since then. It deals with women's health, and women's health issues.

Caring responsibilities

Caring for Someone at Home

Gail Elkington and Gill Harrison, Carers National Association, Hodder & Stoughton, 1996

This is an easy-to-follow, step-by-step guide which covers subjects such as welfare benefits, support groups, how to cope with your needs as well as those of the person you look after, and managing caring and a job. It features real-life experiences of carers and describes how they have resolved their various problems.

Communication issues

The Cost of Communication Breakdown

Janet Walker with research by Clem Henricson, BT Forum Publications, 1995

Interesting research on this subject. The report can be obtained free; call Freefone 0800 800 926.

6

The water's cold: returning after a career break

'The cost of training scientists, engineers and technologists is high. Therefore, if the expertise of qualified women scientists and engineers is underused or lost to the workplace, this represents a financial loss to the nation.' The Rising Tide, 1994, page 2

Today more and more people – men and women – are choosing to take a career break for a variety of reasons.

- You might have to take time off to look after your children, or an elderly or sick relative.
- You might want or need to study, perhaps for a further qualification.
- You might want to accompany your partner on sabbatical leave or a foreign work assignment.

Not surprisingly the vast majority of career breaks are those taken by women when they have a baby or adopt a child. Consequently, although the information in this chapter will be useful for anybody intending to take time out, it will focus on the 'classic' woman returner who takes a career break to start and raise a family and goes back to work when she can.

'What is striking is that very high proportions of women return to work after having a child and that contrary to popular assumptions this is not a new phenomenon. For example, over 90 per cent of women who had a first birth in the late 1950s and early 1960s had returned to work at some stage and among older women the proportions were not much lower: 87 per cent of women who had a first birth in the early 1940s had subsequently returned to employment.' Martin and Roberts, Women and Employment: a lifetime perspective, 1984

Although women have for some time been returning to work while (or after) raising their family, in recent years the number of women going back to work quite soon after having a baby has increased dramatically, and the amount of time they have taken off from work during the child-raising years has decreased. Even so, the impact of new responsibilities and the problems of re-entering employment will still affect most women – and their families.

Whatever the length of your career break, you can eliminate the potentially negative impact of taking a career break and facilitate a smooth return back to work by planning it well in advance, and by implementing certain strategies during your time away from paid employment.

Getting ready to take the plunge

'A scientist or engineer who drops out, even briefly, can easily become a permanent loss to the nation's resources.' Daphne Jackson Memorial Fellowships Trust

When it comes to career breaks, women working in SET have particular advantages and disadvantages.

- The bad news is that a career break can mean you lose touch with the cutting edge of science and technology – even after six months away, you might feel 'left behind'. In addition, with the relatively long training that many SET jobs involve, the optimum time for having a family is usually when your career is at a critical stage, for example when you are taking professional exams or when you are trying to get a permanent research position following postdoctoral work.

- The good news is that your valuable SET expertise makes you worth hanging on to!

It is essential to make sure your employer realises that career breaks make financial, social and academic sense. This may not be an easy task, but women working in SET have an advantage over many other employees simply because training a scientist or engineer from scratch is an extremely expensive business.

Your employer's attitude to career breaks should be clear from the recruitment literature or from your information on terms of employment. You should also be able to gauge the likely reaction to your request for a career break from colleagues.

Many organisations now accept that facilitating career breaks results in sound economic benefits. Here are some arguments in case you need them:

- Many of the most valuable employees will be women.
- It costs far more to recruit and train a replacement, than to allow an experienced professional to take a managed career break (see the quotes on pages 109 and 123).
- Career breaks can provide a source of qualified staff who can provide relief cover at times.
- Career break schemes are relatively easy to run and are cost effective, as the quote from Rank Xerox shows.
- Career break schemes help to attract the best recruits and retain highly trained, top quality staff.

The arguments formerly used against career breaks – career breaks are awkward to implement, can cause staffing problems, and women fail to return – are becoming increasingly irrelevant as the example of forward-thinking organisations demonstrates.

If your employer is not convinced that losing valuable expertise matters, cite companies such as National Westminster Bank, Unilever, and ICI (Imperial Chemical Industries), and the ways in which they benefit from career break schemes. Many companies, even SMEs (small and medium-sized enterprises), find that the costs of implementing career break schemes and 'childcare portfolios' pay for themselves within a few years.

'Rank Xerox: Changing the Culture ... Improving the maternity benefit, and women "phasing in" on return through part-time working has reduced the loss of over 80% of skilled and experienced women, to less than 20%. Over five years, after allowing for the additional cost of the programme, this has brought a "return" of some £1 million through savings in recruitment, retraining and lost productivity ... [Rank Xerox offer] Career Breaks to enable the retention of men and women with skills and training who would otherwise have been lost to the business.' Department of Trade and Industry and Opportunity 2000, Making the Most, Women in science, engineering and technology, Building a workforce for sustained competitiveness, 1995, page 10

Planning your career break

The earlier you plan your career break the better: you will need to plan your return to work well before you leave!

If you are aiming to start a family – are you going to come back to work 'between' children or are you going to spend several years away? One scientist explains her reasoning: 'In my field research was moving so rapidly, I wanted to get back reasonably quickly. I knew I couldn't afford to spend several years out so I deliberately planned to have my children close together. I was lucky – it worked out for me.' Research immunologist working in industry

You will need to start by thinking about who to talk to – and when – about your career break. Build up your own confidence in what you aim to do, try to anticipate possible reactions to your plans, and prepare your answers.

- How easy will it be for someone else to cover your work while you are gone?
- Has anyone in the organisation taken a similar break or are you breaking new ground?

Can you then discuss your plans with your manager(s)? It might be that you could plan your family around a future move into a more 'family-friendly' job.

Once you know that a career break is imminent, don't wait for others to make the arrangements: nobody will care about your career as much as you do. Think of your career break as time *out*, not time *off* and plan accordingly. The following action plan and checklist suggests some of the issues you will need to consider.

Action Plan: Organising your break

❏ Start preparing for your career break well in advance. Find out what the policy is in your organisation, and if necessary, also research what's going on elsewhere. Your professional society or trades union might be able to help your here.

❏ Identify what you would prefer to do. Do you want a complete break and then come back full-time? Or would you prefer a shorter break, perhaps with a phased part-time return to work?

❏ Prepare a well-thought through proposal which demonstrates:
   – what you are requesting
   – how this can be managed
   – the timescale of your break
   – your availability for work during your time away
   – how you aim to stay in touch and up to date
   – the benefits your career break and subsequent return will have for your employer.

Checklist: Before you go ...

Have you ...

❏ consulted the appropriate person about the implications for your pension and national insurance contributions?

❏ made it clear if and how you expect to be available for work within the organisation? For instance, you might work on a special assignment, or cover for someone else, or attend specific meetings

❏ informed your employer that you are willing to do some work from your home?

❏ asked to be offered training courses, seminars or conferences during your time out and/or on your return to work?

❏ checked on systems for keeping in touch with your organisation, your field and your profession on a regular basis?

❏ investigated career counselling before and after your time out?

While you're away

Once you have a family, you'll wonder why you ever thought you were busy before. At this stage it is critical to carve out time for yourself – though every mother knows this is easier said than done. Whether your career break is going to be six months or six years, you must keep your professional life ticking over. The following suggestions come from other women who have been there, done it and survived.

Strategies for success

- 'Keep networking during a career break. Arrange to meet your colleagues regularly. If you can't meet them, phone them, or invite them round to your house for a drink at the weekend. You may feel awkward at first, but it's worth persevering: it makes it easier when you do go back to work. I also instigated "work" topics of conversation to prove I wasn't braindead.' Microbiologist

- 'I made a point of reading my professional journals – the *Geological Magazine* and *Bulletin of Volcanology* – regularly one evening a week while my partner "babysat". I also read the *New Scientist*. It wasn't a lot but it meant I could discuss current developments intelligently when I met my boss.' Geologist

- 'A mentor suggested that I used the years at home to write up my research and publish papers. I followed his advice, although it was a struggle at times. My publications made it easier for me to get a job when I wanted to go back to paid employment.' Research chemist

- 'I organised childcare so that I could attend the meetings of my local AWiSE group. I also went to the annual conference of my professional association, even though I felt out of touch by then. Once I got there, I soon cottoned on to the new issues.' Industrial pharmacologist

- 'I kept up my membership of the Royal Society of Chemistry even though I didn't work for five years.' Industrial chemist

- 'I paid for childcare one day a week and spent it in the library of my local university. I couldn't really afford the time or the money but I looked on it as an investment – and a pleasure!' Research zoologist

- 'I used the time out to study for my professional exams – but it wasn't easy.' Mechanical engineer

- 'I did some self-financed, part-time research – I was fortunate in that I didn't need expensive equipment. It wasn't a lot, but it was something to put on application forms and talk about at interviews.' Research biologist

Once you've taken a career break, the problems and experiences you are likely to encounter when you want to return to work will vary according to your personal circumstances: for example, the length of your career break, what's happened while you have been away, and the extent to which you've kept in contact with the job.

'In the 1990s women returners have been the major source of recruitment. They have taken more than 80 % of all new jobs.' Women's National Commission, Women in the 90s, 1994, page 54

Edging in carefully

The water looks cold and so you fancy edging in slowly?

Many women find that a phased return to work suits them best. Fortunately more organisations will now accommodate flexible working arrangements such as those discussed on page 107. After a career break, the most common flexible working arrangements include:

- part-time work, either on a long-term basis, or slowly building up your hours to full-time
- job sharing (two people share the responsibilities (and salary!) of one permanent full-time position)
- working from home – some or all of the time
- flexible hours.

You might have to argue the case for some of these. Working from home, for instance, has a number of limitations and is still relatively unpopular with many employers (and other employees!) despite the advantages of low overheads, modern communications and high productivity. Part-time work – and job sharing – is often regarded with suspicion even though many employers find that pro-rata productivity in terms of quality and quantity of work is higher than for one person in a full-time job. The books on page 138 will help you to marshal your arguments in favour of more flexible ways of working.

Many women find that the costs of working – childcare, transport and other expenses – swallow up their salary. You could look on this period as an investment in yourself: particularly if you still have several decades of working life ahead of you. The long-term gains will make it all worthwhile.

'At times in those early days I wondered why I was bothering! Going back to work part-time involved so much organisation and the cost of the childminder for two children meant I wasn't left with much at the end of the month. But I loved the work. Six years down the line I'm in a fascinating job with a lot of responsibility, earning good money. I'm still part-time (although I've increased my hours) but I know that I can go full-time whenever I want.' Research immunologist working in industry

Jumping in with a splash

Many women can't wait to get back to work: 'After the birth of my second child I suffered from postnatal depression: it was an effort even to get dressed. I felt guilty about wanting to go back to work. In the end it was my doctor who suggested that not only I but my family could benefit from me resuming my career. While I'm not suggesting it's the answer for every woman, it was the best thing I ever did.' Academic research scientist

Most women would agree that the key factor in a successful (and relatively guilt-free) return to work is good childcare.

Chapter 5 outlines the childcare options in more detail. If, despite everything, you still feel guilty about going back to work, remind yourself of the benefits that all your family will ultimately derive from your career: your partner, if you have one, will not have to bear the sole responsibility for supporting the family financially, and your children will benefit from a positive role model.

Being pushed

Divorced? Widowed? Or needing to make ends meet? Economic necessity and rising male unemployment mean that women with family responsibilities are increasingly taking on the role of breadwinner. The days when women worked for pin money have long since disappeared and many families now depend on two incomes. Sadly, many parents (and particularly lone parents) may feel that the difficulties of getting a decent well-paid job are insurmountable and resort to work well below their skills and abilities, but women should not undersell themselves.

If you are 'forced' back to paid work before you're ready for it, you may have some specific problems you'll need to overcome.

- Your return may be prompted by short-term needs rather than long-term career goals.
- You may lack the financial resources to allow you to spend time retraining.
- You may lack confidence.

Good careers guidance and counselling can help you to tackle the first problem and point you in the direction of ways and means in which you can begin to overcome the second. If you can afford to invest in quality training for yourself now, it will pay dividends in the future. (See also the sections on retraining on pages 130-36 of this chapter, and the whole of Chapter 2, which also covers sources of finance.) That leaves the third problem ...

Most women returners – should that read most women? – suffer from a lack of confidence: the all-important functions of home-making and childrearing have too low a status in our society. As a consequence, women who take time out often undervalue their previous work experience, discount their skills acquired whilst managing a home and a family, and feel they have very little to offer. Even the most self-confident will also find that their knowledge and skills need updating after a career break.

If this is true of you, how do you build or rebuild your confidence? See which of the following strategies might work for you.

Strategies for success

- Work out what you *really* want to do next. Not what you think you ought to do, or what other people feel you should do. Then think about how you could achieve your objectives.

- Consider enrolling on a personal development, assertiveness or confidence-building course. (These often form an important part of good retraining programmes.)

- Books can help (some titles are suggested on page 138).

- Surround yourself with people who believe in you. Until you are feeling more confident, reduce your interaction with those who don't.

- Think about your strengths. If you haven't already done so, draw up a SWOT analysis (see page 14). When you are faced with a blank space for strengths, analyse the transferable skills and competences you've acquired from running a home and a family over the last few years:

  Time and organisation management

  – the ability to prioritise

  – fast and accurate decision-making

  – managing a tight budget

  – the ability to hold down a demanding and stressful management role.

  Communication skills

  – in negotiation

  – team working

  – conflict resolution!

- Don't forget the work you may have taken on outside the home: have you been the treasurer of a PTA, or worked as a school governor for example? Voluntary work such as this may have developed skills such as:

  – working on committees

  – making presentations

  – chairing meetings

  – accounting and budgeting with scarce resources.

- Highlight the greater maturity, fresh approach and enthusiasm(!) you can bring to a job after spending time out.

- Work out ways of getting over your 'development areas' (or weaknesses). Then start analysing what opportunities are open to you.

- Invest in yourself if you can: there's no better investment. Updating your skills through educational and training courses can pay dividends, making you more employable – and more valuable to an employer.

- Find yourself an effective mentor – see Chapter 4 – and network.

- To quote the old cliché, nothing succeeds like success. Make sure the challenges you set yourself are difficult but achievable – and remember the 80:20 syndrome (see page 53).

- Force yourself to speak up in meetings and ask questions at seminars and conferences. Don't be afraid to be noticed.

- Act the part of the SET professional that you are. This means dressing appropriately – your external image does matter, whether you like it or not. This doesn't mean you have to become a power-dressed clone, but you might like to develop a distinctive style that will help you progress in your chosen direction. Revitalising your image is another investment: looking the part helps you to feel the part.

- Don't worry too much about getting to the top of the mountain – just take the next step, and the next, looking back now and again to congratulate yourself on how far you've come.

Action Plan: Getting to where you want to go

It can help to write yourself an action plan - the one on page 15 provides a good basis to work from. At regular intervals:

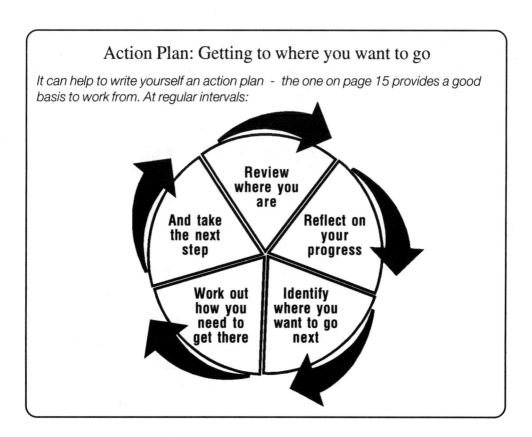

Review where you are

Reflect on your progress

Identify where you want to go next

Work out how you need to get there

And take the next step

What advice would other SET returners give?

- 'Go easy on yourself – everybody finds it hard at first.' Research zoologist
- 'The first weeks are the most difficult.' Project manager
- 'Don't allow yourself to feel stupid about learning about new techniques or technologies. Don't be intimidated: how long did it take the person teaching you to learn?' Systems engineer
- 'You will feel pressurised, but don't be afraid to ask for help. People love showing you how knowledgeable they are.' Research biologist
- 'Build up a support structure at home – childminders, neighbours, friends.' Civil engineer
- 'Anticipate the school holidays – or they'll come as a nasty shock.' Industrial pharmacologist
- 'Don't try to do everything so the family doesn't "suffer". Delegate tasks to the family – it's character-forming!' Software engineer
- 'I knew I was out of date, but I did some concentrated reading of research papers, books and journals. After that, I felt I had a handle of things again.' Physicist
- 'Don't expect too much too soon. Be patient and don't lose hope. It'll take time.' Electrical engineer

And finally:

'Once I took the plunge, it was so easy. Now I wonder why it took me so long and what I was so worried about. Take that first step. You'll be surprised at what you can do.' Senior programmer

Retraining

In this technological era when the most advanced technology can be out of date when it is barely installed, most women who wish to return to work will need to either update their skills and knowledge or even retrain.

A commitment to a retraining or educational scheme can not only increase your confidence, but also demonstrate your credibility to future employers.

If you wish to retrain locally, you can find out information about local courses and schemes from your library, careers guidance service, TAPs, or TEC/LEC, or by contacting nearby colleges and universities directly, and from your nearest Regional Office of the Open University. Many courses, such as the NOW (New Opportunities for Women) course run by the University of Hertfordshire, are aimed specifically at women returners who wish to explore the options available, improve their skills and qualifications, and plan for the future.

It is critical that you have good careers guidance before starting a course, and reliable childcare organised: your confidence can be badly knocked if you are forced to drop out for whatever reason. Women-only courses might help to boost your confidence if necessary.

When contemplating a course, work out what you need. For example, check whether the one you're considering offers:

- careers guidance and counselling about short-term and long-term goals
- recognised qualifications
- childcare facilities (if necessary)
- teaching hours that fit in with school hours and terms
- plenty of hands-on experience with new technology and equipment that are actually being used in the workplace!
- work placements or contacts with appropriate companies
- job search and interview skills.

If your local educational institution does not provide what you require, talk to the management there and find out why not. A lot of women discover that they can get their needs met if they demonstrate that there is a demand and refuse to take no for an answer.

Many courses are specifically aimed at women returners: there is a dazzling range on offer from straightforward Access courses in engineering and technology, to a motor vehicle electronics and microprocessors course, to postgraduate certificates in education (technical). Several courses are designed to enable women to acquire scientific and technical qualifications for the first time.

Chapter 2 covers education, training and lifelong learning in more detail, while the rest of this chapter discusses various opportunities, schemes and fellowships that are particularly appropriate for women returners.

Open learning

If you cannot manage to get to a college or university for whatever reason, you could consider an open learning course. This means that you study at your own pace (and mainly in your own home) using multimedia materials such as books, radio and television programmes, CD-Roms, computer software, television and email. There is also the possibility of tutorials, residential schools and counselling services. The Open University was the first UK university to use 'open' and 'distance' learning methods, but many colleges and universities now offer this facility.

This could also be a option to explore if you are living abroad, perhaps because of your partner's job, or if you have a physical disability. It might also be something to consider if you want to enter SET for the first time, or investigate a completely new or different area of science and technology.

As a woman returner, you will probably find open learning has several advantages.

- For many courses, you will not need any prior qualifications.
- You can get back into studying gradually.
- Many open learning courses are designed on a modular basis so you can study as much or as little as you want, and you can choose your courses as you go along and gain confidence.
- It's very flexible – you can fit studying in with your other commitments.

Naturally, open learning also has its drawbacks.

- You might feel lonely and want the stimulation of fellow students.
- Self-discipline is critical: will you find yourself continually relegating your studying to the bottom of 'your list' because of your other commitments?

The Open University (OU)

The OU is now very well known for its supported open learning courses across a whole range of subjects and at all levels. Most people have heard about the OU's excellent science and technology courses ranging from foundation courses such as 'Living with technology', 'Using mathematics' and 'Discovering science', to second, third and fourth level courses in mathematics, science and technology. However, are you aware of its expanding range of higher degree courses? If you are thinking of using your experience in a different area or job, you could do a Professional Certificate in Management, for example, or an MBA (Technology Management), or a Diploma in Pollution Control. Alternatively how about a Postgraduate Diploma in Manufacturing, Management and Technology, or an MSc in Computing for Commerce and Industry, or an MSc in Environmental Decision-Making?

Find out more about these and other SET courses from your local Regional Office or from:

The Course Reservations and Sales Centre
The Open University
Walton Hall
Milton Keynes
MK7 6YZ

Prospectus request hotline: 01908 858 585; 24-hour OU hotline: 0800 733 766; website: http://www.open.ac.uk

---

There are several other awards and fellowships which are well suited to women with family commitments. At the time of writing, these included the following.

The Daphne Jackson Memorial Fellowships Trust

If you:

- want to go back to work after a career break of at least three years
- have at least a first degree in engineering or science
- are normally resident in the UK
- are highly motivated
- are prepared to work on and submit an appropriate research proposal

then you might be eligible for a Daphne Jackson Fellowship.

Daphne Jackson was Britain's first woman professor of physics and was a lifelong campaigner, encouraging girls and women into engineering and science. Appalled by the waste of taxpayers' money when talented women were unable to return to their chosen fields after a career break, she launched her inspired Fellowships Scheme in 1985.

After her death in 1991, the scheme became the Daphne Jackson Memorial Fellowships Trust. Since its inception, the scheme has enabled over 50 highly qualified and trained women engineers and scientists to restart their careers after a break.

Fellowships are arranged throughout the UK, and typically last two years. They are carried out on a flexible part-time basis to enable Fellows to meet their family commitments. The Fellowship includes retraining and updating (including approximately 100 hours per year of instruction in new technologies), plus a substantial guided research or development project at an accessible university.

Candidates for fellowships have to contact an appropriate university science or engineering faculty to discuss a possible area for investigation. This can be either in a previous field of expertise or in a new area. Fellowship topics have included 'Trace elements in pre-eclampsia and hyperactivity', 'Analytic and computer modelling of low-energy electron impact ionisation at surfaces' and 'The physics of the modern Olympic bow'. Projects should be relevant to present-day needs so as to enhance the Fellow's future employment opportunities.

In the Government's official response to *The Rising Tide* report it commended 'the excellent work' done by the Daphne Jackson Memorial Fellowships Trust which exists to bring 'women returners up to speed and to retrain and update their knowledge in science and engineering'. Perhaps even more eloquent is the comment by a Daphne Jackson Fellow: 'After being at home with the children you lose confidence in yourself and wonder if you can do it any more. I approached the Daphne Jackson Trust in despair. They were wonderful and gave me the positive support I needed to get back into research.

I love it. I'm where I want to be. I can't tell you what that means to me. I praise the Trust in the highest possible terms.' Dr Deborah Oppenheim (profiled on page 180), Daphne Jackson Fellow conducting research into airborne remote sensing of coastal phytoplankton populations using the Compact Airborne Spectrographic Imager (CASI). Dr Veronica Bennett, another Daphne Jackson Fellow, is profiled on page 135.

Find out more from:

The Daphne Jackson Memorial Fellowships Trust
Department of Physics
University of Surrey
Guildford
Surrey
GU2 5XH
Tel: 01483 259 166; fax: 01483 259 501; website: http://www.sst.ph.ic.ac.uk/trust

The Wellcome Trust Re-entry Fellowships

The Wellcome Trust has established a re-entry fellowship scheme as part of an initiative to make careers in science more attractive to women, and to encourage scientists back into the field after a career break – or even a change of career. These competitive fellowships are full-time for four years (or possibly part-time), and are intended to cover retraining, as well as the core costs of suitable research projects. You can obtain further details of these and other Wellcome Trust fellowships from:

The Wellcome Trust
183 Euston Road
London NW1 2BE
Tel: 0171 611 8438

Biotechnology and Biological Sciences Research Council

The BBSRC offers several postdoctoral research fellowships schemes which aim to accommodate candidates 'seeking a flexible working arrangement (e.g. part-time)'. The Council welcomes applications from candidates who wish to use a fellowship to 're-establish themselves in research after a career break or other period of absence from active research'. The contact details of the BBSRC are given on page 151.

Engineering and Physical Sciences Research Council

The EPSRC are offering a number of five-year, part-time PhD studentships to encourage people (who are not in paid employment) to return to research after a career break due to family commitments. Following completion of five years' part-time study, students will be permitted a further two years in which to write up and submit their thesis. The contact details for the EPSRC are given on page 151.

Dr Veronica Bennett, research fellow in ecology

Dr Veronica Bennett is in her mid 40s. She is currently a Daphne Jackson Fellow attached to Lucy Cavendish College at the University of Cambridge. Based in the Department of Zoology, she is conducting research in insect ecology, specifically on insects associated with bramble. She has three sons, currently aged 11, nine and four years.

'Is that where you worked when you were a lady, Mummy?'
Pointing out the University of Bristol Medical School, my four-year-old son's innocent enquiry summed it up for me and for many other women: I had two degrees and a wealth of research experience in the control of cell division, having worked in both the UK and abroad; I had been at some of the best institutes in the world, and yet since I had taken a career break to have a family I no longer had any status. After ten years I felt invisible and inaudible. This makes a hopeless standpoint from which to apply for appropriate employment.

In returning to a scientific career, the problems of updating knowledge and skills are obvious. I have found that loss of confidence is actually the greater hurdle to be overcome. It interferes with the retraining process on every level, from interacting with colleagues and potential employers/grant providers to trusting yourself to prioritise sensibly in the limited amount of study time. People take you at your own valuation – who will believe in you if you are no longer able to believe in yourself? There is a vicious circle to be broken.

This is the enormous value of the Daphne Jackson Memorial Fellowships Trust. I would not have attempted to return to research had it not been for the advert for a Fellowship to be held locally at Lucy Cavendish College. My husband told me about it while I was bathing the baby. From that moment I never looked back.

The Trust is very supportive from the start, but the retraining process starts with preparing the application. Once your eligibility for a Fellowship has been established, it is up to you to find a supervisor and a research project, and put together a programme of study. The choice of supervisor and project are very important. My initial discussions with members of the University led me to reject my first idea of going back to my original research area – cell biology had become highly competitive and research was moving forward so fast that it would be almost impossible to achieve anything significant working part-time. Cell biology also needs high-tech equipment and expensive materials, and I was conscious that these Fellowships carry with them only minimal funds, and that I would be unable to move to find a job. I wanted something that I could continue under my own steam if necessary.

The fact that our village boasts a number of magnificent bramble hedges was not the only reason for my choice of project. Everybody removes the bramble – gardeners, farmers and even managers of conservation areas. Yet it has the potential to be a life support system for a variety of wildlife from small mammals to insects, providing shelter, and in season, leaves, flowers and fruits for food. It may shelter predators of agricultural pests, and may be a cheaper and faster means of attracting wildlife to areas of land reclamation than the usual tree planting schemes. The project therefore has practical applications, which should increase my options for future employment.

When I eventually started work again, everything was different. In my last employment there were no faxes, email or Internet, and the only computers were mainframes. The changes aren't all positive, though. Communications with the States may be easier, but all the doors on the corridor are kept locked, so there is less interaction on a departmental level. Money is tighter, too. I now find myself frustrated by lack of time rather than lack of stimulation, and colleagues do not always appreciate the constraints of working part-time. However, throughout everything, the Trust and the College have been very helpful and encouraging. They have met most of the problems before! These Fellowships give you permission not to know all the answers, recognise your need for training and give you the chance and the means to do it.

It is vital to survival as a working mother to know that your children are safe, happy and stimulated when you are not with them. Thus when the local playscheme folded half way through my fellowship, a replacement had to be organised. That presents challenges on a completely different level and time scale from research, and it is exhilarating to see immediate results from your problem-solving – a working playscheme and happy children.

It is amazing to look back and see how far this Fellowship has brought me. Three years ago I was at home, loving my children, but terminally frustrated intellectually. Now I am attempting to do the equivalent of two and a half full-time jobs at once – running a home and family, a physically and intellectually demanding research project, and chairing the committee running the out-of-school playscheme.

The overall effect on the family has been positive. My oldest son now looks on me with more respect, and is going to be a scientist when he grows up. However, I am in no danger of becoming over-confident: when I offered to lead a 'Bug hunt' for the playscheme, one mother confided 'Oh, I'm so glad it's you doing it – I was afraid it was going to be an expert!'

Further information

Most of the Research Councils now provide support for returners in different ways: for example, the Natural Environment Research Council (NERC) has introduced a one-year Fellowship scheme intended to enable high-level environmental scientists to return to research following a family or career break. The contact details of all the Research Councils are listed on pages 151-52.

The Women Returners' Network

The Women Returners' Network aims to facilitate women's re-entry into education, training and employment through promoting and disseminating good practice and encouraging sponsors, decision-makers and gatekeepers to address the needs of women returners. Amongst other activities, it has a helpline, and publishes books and resource sheets and a quarterly newsletter.

The Women Returners' Network
100 Park Village East
London NW1 3SR
Tel: 0171 468 2290; fax: 0171 380 0123

Lucy Cavendish College, University of Cambridge

Lucy Cavendish College is part of the University of Cambridge. Uniquely, it specialises in the education of mature women undergraduate and graduate students. Some bursaries may be available for those studying either for a first degree, or for a further degree, and occasionally research fellowships may be awarded. For a prospectus contact:

Lucy Cavendish College
Lady Margaret Road
Cambridge
CB3 0BU
Tel: 01223 330 280; fax: 01223 332 178; email: lcc–admissions@lists.cam.ac.uk

Professional societies

Many of the professional societies and other organisations offer advice and information on career break schemes and/or allow people on a career break a reduced membership subscription. The Women's Engineering Society, for example, aims to 'sustain contacts with women engineers on career breaks and facilitates their return to paid employment by keeping them informed of progress within the profession'.

The Useful Addresses section beginning on page 207 includes many of the SET professional societies. Contact them directly to see what they can offer.

Returning to work

Returning to Work: a guide for lone parents

Written and published by the National Council for One Parent Families, revised 1996

A basic information pack to help lone parents create and develop a career plan.

Back to Work: a resource guide for women returners

Gill Sargent, The Industrial Society, 1995

A brief guide with useful names, addresses, and other advice.

Women Mean Business: a practical guide for women returners

Caroline Bamford and Catherine McCarthy, BBC Books, 1991

Although some of the information is now inevitably out of date, this 'practical guide for women returners' is a positive book and covers many of the areas which concern women going back into paid employment: confidence-building strategies, getting a job and childcare options.

Flexible working patterns

The Complete Guide to Working from Home

Sue Read, Headline, 1992

A straightforward outline of the available options, illustrated by case studies.

Home is Where the Office is: a practical handbook for teleworking from home

Andrew Bibby, Headway/Hodder & Stoughton, 1991

This book discusses the pros and cons of teleworking.

The Teleworking Handbook: new ways to work in the information society

Imogen Bertin and Alan Denbigh, TCA (Telework, Telecottage and Telecentre Association), 1996

Comprehensive and up-to-date advice from enthusiastic teleworkers.

Job Sharing: a practical guide

Pam Walton, New Ways to Work, 1995

Useful for both employees and employers.

Building confidence

A Woman in Your Own Right: assertiveness and you

Anne Dickson, Quartet, 1982

Now over 15 years old, but *the* classic book on assertiveness for women.

Springboard Women's Development Workbook

Liz Willis and Jenny Daisley, Hawthorn Press, 3rd edition 1993

This workbook provides a basis for systematically reviewing career options and key aspects of personal development including assertiveness, setting goals, and finding support for women to work through issues. It contains practical advice and confidence-boosting strategies. The Consultancy also run a three-month Women's Development course; for further information contact:

Springboard Consultancy
PO Box 69
Stroud
Gloucester
GL5 5EE
Tel: 01453 878 540; fax: 01453 872 363

Unemployment

Out of Work – A Family Affair

Anne Lovell, Sheldon Press, 1996

A quick read but makes some useful points about how to cope with the stresses and strains when a member of the family is without paid work.

Training opportunities

Returning to Work: a directory of education and training for women

Women Returners' Network, Paul Chapman, 8th edition 1996

Intended for women seeking information on returning to education, training and employment, this directory lists over 1700 courses, as well as information on guidance services, grants and childcare.

Second Chances

Compiled and published by Careers and Occupational Information Centre (COIC), 11th edition 1997

A guide to adult education, training and employment opportunities in the UK, Europe and abroad. Obtainable from COIC, whose address is on page 208.

Women into Science and Engineering: awards, courses and visits

Engineering Council (published annually)

A useful booklet compiled by the WISE (Women Into Science and Engineering) Campaign, which includes information on a wide variety of courses at different levels, career breaks and bursaries.

7

Academic research: a long-term future on a short-term contract?

'Society stands to gain if more people move more freely back and forth among the private and public institutions which create wealth for the nation by pushing back the boundaries of scientific and technical knowledge. For this to happen, we need better management of the careers of younger researchers.' Sir Robert May, Royal Society Research Professor and from September 1995 Chief Scientific Adviser to the Government, in 'US lessons on short-term contracts', New Scientist, 14 March 1992

One of the many paradoxes of society today is that as most of us look forward to a longer life – and for women, a longer working life – work itself has become more short term. Although some still cherish the idea of a job for life, the pace of change is such that more and more people are employed for limited or specified periods of time.

This has obviously always been a fact of life for the self-employed, who expect to spend some of their time negotiating for the next piece of work. What is different, however, is that the practice of employing people for specified periods in business and industry is now commonplace, whilst in universities the numbers of staff employed on short-term or fixed-term contracts have mushroomed. (For ease of reading, the adjective 'short-term' will be used in the rest of this chapter to cover both short-term and fixed-term contracts.)

On the plus side, this expansion has resulted in an overall increase in the number of people working at the cutting edge of science and technology, but on the debit side these expansions have often occurred without strategic planning, sometimes resulting in a situation which is far from ideal.

In 1980, there were 8000 contract researchers employed in UK universities; there are now 28 000, 25 000 of whom are employed in the 'old' universities. The proportion of contract researchers had grown to 44% of all research and teaching staff in the 'old' universities by 1994/95. In some institutions, such as University College London, they actually outnumber permanent staff. The graphs opposite indicate the scale of the situation. They are taken from the article by Clare Goodess, 'Short contracts and short termism', *Science and Public Affairs*, Winter 1996.

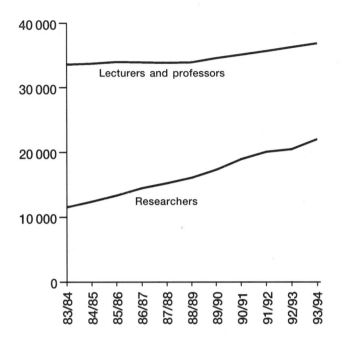

Staff numbers in the 'old' UK universities, 1983-84 to 1993-94.

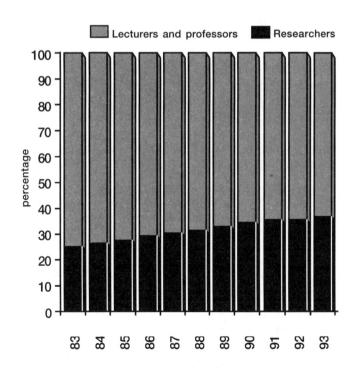

Research staff as a percentage of all teaching and research staff in the 'old' UK universities, 1983-84 to 1993-94.

This chapter concentrates specifically on the effect that the dramatic expansion of short-term contracts in academia has had on women, although many of the comments are clearly equally applicable to men, and to people in business and industrial organisations.

The issue of short-term contracts is a complex one and much depends on the exact nature of the contract and the career ambitions of the holder. Some short-term contracts, for example the Royal Society's University Research Fellowships, are an excellent way to start a scientific research career and holders almost always go straight into prestigious jobs at good universities. At the other end of the spectrum, some researchers on a short-term contract may not fulfil their early promise or may discover that their talents and inclinations are not best suited to a career in research and so decide to 'branch out' in a different direction. In the 'middle', there are many good researchers on short-term contracts whose careers would advance more smoothly if the 'system' managed them better.

This chapter aims to provide you with an awareness of the advantages and disadvantages of short-term contracts in academia that will help you to avoid the pitfalls and exploit the opportunities on offer. It should enable you to develop accurate expectations so that you are able to make an informed decision about what an institution might be offering you.

The advantages and disadvantages of short-term contracts

The profile of Dr Victoria Nield on page 149 demonstrates how a short-term contract can be a powerful and effective springboard to a fulfilling career within a university. As the following comments indicate, the careers of many scientists and engineers have benefitted from one or two short-term contracts.

- 'A short-term contract can be a very useful career starting point for a young scientist. You can find out whether you actually enjoy working in research or in academia, and you can learn valuable skills such as proposal and report writing, working in teams, and giving presentations. Short-term contracts can broaden your experience and offer you a variety of opportunities. The problems really only start when you become a 30-something.' Research chemist

- 'Short-term contracts keep you on your toes and force you to live in the present.' Research zoologist

- 'Some contract researchers value the flexibility and freedom that short-term contracts offer.' Physicist

- 'Short-term contracts can enable the employer to hold on to researchers with expertise until a permanent post can be offered.' University professor

- 'They can be an effective way of getting new projects off the ground, and can make significant contributions.' Computer scientist

- 'Short-term contracts can be a useful opening for foreign researchers.' Materials scientist

- 'Many institutions would have difficulty meeting their teaching and research objectives without the operational and strategic flexibility of short-term contracts.' Crystallographer

- 'Short-term contracts ensure that the research community is constantly revitalised with new ideas and new blood.' University professor

Still short-term contracts are widely perceived as having disadvantages.

- 'When you're younger you're too inexperienced; when you're older you're too expensive.' Research chemist

- 'I can't say where I'll be living or working in three months' time. I feel I'm a nomad.' Research biologist

- 'I took six months off between contracts to have a baby and had to go back to the starting point on the pay scale.' Crystallographer

- 'The building society was reluctant to give me a mortgage. How can you do any long-term life planning when you're suffering from short-term insecurity?' Electronic engineer

- 'On many short contracts you only have about 12–18 months of really productive work if you deduct the time spent setting up, designing the experiments and getting into the project, and the final year where you're distracted by getting the next job or the next grant.' Research zoologist

- 'I have low status, low morale and I'm on low pay. The only thing that's high is the number of hours I work.' Research biologist

- 'The chances of getting a permanent appointment can be as tough as 1 in 10 in some university departments. I'm leaving to work in the City!' Mathematician

The 1995 'Dainton Report' (see page 153) took a pessimistic view: 'The major defect is that contract researchers in the sciences are now approximately as numerous as established staff and in these disciplines, are relatively disadvantaged in terms of career progression, salary, continuity of work, access to facilities available to established staff and participation in the affairs of the university which employs them ... Furthermore the perception by others in this group as almost an underclass can only be a deterrent to able young students in science.' House of Lords Select Committee on Science and Technology, *Academic Research Careers for Graduate Scientists Report*, 1995, page 31

It seems there are still a considerable number of drawbacks to the present system, although it must be emphasised that there is now a growing initiative aimed at identifying and removing some of the structural obstacles and problems related to short-term contracts in academia. Clare Goodess discusses some of the problems, and indicates the emerging solutions.

Clare Goodess, research climatologist

Clare Goodess is in her late 30s and has spent her working life on short-term contracts. The following extracts are taken from her article 'Short contracts and short termism' published in the Winter 1996 issue of Science and Public Affairs.

In 1982 I started work as a contract researcher in the internationally renowned Climatic Research Unit at the University of East Anglia. Almost 15 years on I am still here and so able to reflect on how attitudes to university contract research and global warming have changed over time.

Global warming is now firmly established on the political agenda. The growing interest in climate change is reflected in the increased funding coming into the Climatic Research Unit. With 24 research staff and 12 postgraduate students, it is now larger than it has ever been in its 25-year history. The majority of these staff are employed on income from research grants which we have gone out and won. The growth of the Unit in this fashion typifies the trend in other institutions.

So what does it mean to be employed as a contract researcher rather than as a permanent member of staff? In my case, it has meant being employed on a series of 40 contracts, ranging in length from one to 21 months. Some of these contracts have not been reviewed until the last moment, or even a few days after the previous contract expired. Being a contract researcher means signing a waiver clause so I cannot even consider claiming unfair dismissal if a contract is not renewed. I am excluded from the major decision-making bodies within the university. After 15 years I am still categorised as a temporary employee. All of this contributes towards my feeling of low status. Insecurity and low status inevitably lead to low morale. I fully sympathise with a colleague who described himself as a 'lower form of life'.

Yet in comparison with some contract researchers, I have been lucky. I have always had excellent professional support from my supervisors and colleagues. I've been promoted. I haven't had gaps between contracts or had to take a cut in salary in order to get a new contract. I no longer have to waive my rights to statutory redundancy payments. This is no more than anyone might expect of a reasonable employer, but sadly it does not reflect the experience of all contract researchers.

Recognition of these problems is growing, however, in both academic and political circles. The most recent indication that practical solutions of the problems are being sought is the *Concordat on Contract Research Staff Career Management* launched in

1996 by a group of employers: (the Committee of Vice-Chancellors and Principals of the Universities in the UK (CVCP); the Standing Conference of Principals (SCOP); the Committee of Scottish Higher Education Principals (COSHEP); and funding bodies (the six Research Councils, the Royal Society and the British Academy). The Concordat offers contract researchers the prospect of parity with other academic staff in terms of conditions of employment, better career planning and access to training and staff development facilities. I believe that the Concordat could have gone further, by demanding an end to the use of waiver clauses, for example. But it does at least indicate that the employers and major funding bodies have finally recognised their responsibilities towards a large group of people who make an invaluable contribution to UK science.

Like many contract researchers, I tend to focus on the negative aspects when asked about my job. However, I wouldn't have stayed in contract research for so long if the rewards of being so actively involved in my chosen research area didn't provide sufficient compensation. It has been particularly satisfying working in a research area which was relatively new and difficult to get funding for when I started work, but which is now well funded and the topic of widespread political and popular debate. I would advise anyone contemplating a career in contract research to be fully aware of the potential problems beforehand and, once employed, to get involved in the various formal and informal groups and networks which provide essential support and which are working to improve the employment conditions for research staff.

(See page 146 for further information on the *Concordat*.)

A female problem?

Whether or not the advantages currently outweigh the disadvantages, what does seem to be true at the current time is that there is a higher probability of women encountering problems relating to short-term contracts than of men encountering them. The reason for this is highlighted in the Dainton Report: 'It remains true that, for every discipline, the percentage of men in permanent posts is always greater than the percentage of men in contract posts. For women the reverse is always observed.' House of Lords Select Committee on Science and Technology, *Academic Research Careers for Graduate Scientists Report*, 1995, page 14

This factor is compounded by others.

- The age when a woman might be applying for or working on a short-term contract will often coincide with the time she might be considering having a family.
- Women in dual career families may be less mobile.
- Older women who have taken a career break may find it increasingly difficult to obtain further contracts to match their age and experience which makes them 'too expensive'.

- Women may be ambitious, but more realistic in their ambitions than men. Many women tend to wait until they feel they have a strong CV, and even then may make fewer job and fellowship applications. Men often apply for positions for which they might be insufficiently qualified or experienced and therefore 'fail', but their very application demonstrates their commitment to science, they acquire valuable interview practice, and they become more visible. Women are often more fearful of failure than men.

All this might sound discouraging, but the good news is that these issues have been raised at the highest levels, and ways of managing the 'important national resource' that short-term researchers represent are being actively explored.

Furthermore, employers also see disadvantages in short-term contracts: they may have to spend more time and money training and recruiting staff, and they may fail to attract the 'best and brightest' graduates. This has meant that they too are looking for solutions to alleviate the situation and it is likely that there will be changes for the better within the next few years.

In order to overcome some of the drawbacks for women, *The Rising Tide* report emphasises the need for the removal of age limits and mode of study restrictions, and promotes the practice of 'portable' fellowships 'to individuals rather than to institutions so that the holder can choose his or her place of work' (page 41). It also suggests flexibility with regard to the length of the contract – perhaps allowing researchers to use a three-year grant over five years, for instance – so that maternity leave and part-time working are possible.

The way forward

A Concordat on Contract Research Staff Career Management

In 1996 the bodies mentioned in Clare Goodess's article signed *A Concordat on Contract Research Staff Career Management* which aimed to improve the situation by providing a recommended framework for the career management of contract research staff in universities and colleges. The Concordat recognised the problems and opportunities presented by the existing situation and made detailed recommendations for improving the position of short-term contract researchers, although it stated that 'an established career in academia or, exclusively, academic research, is realistic only for a minority'. The recommendations included the following:

'This Concordat sets standards for the career management and conditions of employment of researchers employed by universities and colleges on fixed-term or similar contracts and funded through research grant or analogous schemes ... the framework for the more effective career management of contract staff should be based on ... promoting the active personnel and career management of contract researchers, recognising the important contribution they make to the success of their employing

institutions, including the dissemination of research results and new techniques ... A key element is an assurance of equal opportunities and the elimination of practices linked to the short-term nature of contracts which indirectly discriminate against women. Maternity leave and pay provisions for contract staff should be in line with provisions for established staff, subject to the fixed-term period of the employment contract.'
Concordat on Contract Research Staff Career Management, 1996, pages 1–6

Aiming high

To summarise, if you are embarking on a postdoctoral fellowship or other type of short-term contract as the first stage of an academic career, you need to know exactly what this entails and how to get the most out of the situation – in other words what is the 'best practice' in short-term contracts?

The checklist on page 148 will give you some idea of the issues you need to explore and the questions you need to ask in an interview situation. In addition, don't forget to enquire about the institution's policy on:

- teaching and other duties
- the possibility of additional earning opportunities
- waiver clauses
- any promotion prospects
- the way in which your published research and other achievements will be recognised.

Similarly, it should be made clear that many of the SET funding bodies such as the Research Councils are deeply concerned about the lack of career structure and other problems which can arise in some short-term contracts, but are limited in what they can do by the extremely tight budgets on which they are forced to operate. Many do, however, have a statement of objectives which you can obtain. The Association of University Teachers (AUT) also has information on good employment practice (see page 153).

Points to bear in mind

- The university, not the funding body, is your temporary employer, and so is responsible for your contract. But you should know who is funding the research. One research project might be funded by two or three different organisations.

- Become aware of the limitations and the opportunities provided by your particular position and work to overcome the limitations and get yourself into a position where you are able to take advantage of the opportunities.

- Try to avoid taking on a succession of short-term contracts unless it suits you: be very aware of what is happening both inside and outside your particular field, and what skills and experience are in demand now, and what may be in demand this time next year and further into the future.

- Keep training and diversifying your skills so that you are employable outside university – see Chapter 8.

- Many jobs on short-term contracts are listed in the major journals such as *Science*, *Nature* and *The Times Higher Education Supplement*. These and other professional publications across the SET spectrum will be the major sources of information on what positions are available in both UK and overseas organisations.

- Accept that at some time you may be subject to an 'up-or-out' decision. In other words, you have to be prepared to move to another university or research institute, or outside academia.

Checklist: Short-term contracts – best practice

You might want to find out about whether staff on short-term contracts are offered the same or similar conditions of employment as permanent staff with regard to:

- ❑ salary scales
- ❑ provisions of holiday entitlement, sick leave, compassionate leave, etc.
- ❑ pension, maternity and redundancy rights
- ❑ access to facilities
- ❑ training and development opportunities
- ❑ appropriate representation on decision-making bodies within the department and the university.

In addition, short-term contract staff should be offered:

- ❑ regular reviews and appraisals
- ❑ sound career planning and guidance, and in particular effective counselling if they are unlikely to obtain a permanent post within academia
- ❑ smooth transitions and bridging arrangements between contracts
- ❑ retraining and re-entry routes after career breaks
- ❑ increased training opportunities for greater career flexibility
- ❑ continuity of rights of entitlement from contract to contract and university to university.

Appointments should not be restricted by chronological age limits but rather should take academic stage (i.e. accomplishments) into account. A person who had a late start should not be penalised by arbitrary age limits on eligibility for grants, etc.

There should be a clear definition of a short-term contract worker's duties and responsibilities.

There should be longer-term (i.e. four- or five-year) fellowships for the most able.

Dr Victoria Nield, lecturer in condensed matter physics

Dr Victoria Nield is in her late 20s and obtained her current lectureship at the University of Kent whilst employed elsewhere on a short-term contract.

Physics is about hard problems that need solving and that's what attracted me to the subject. After my first degree, I was going to work in industry but at a late stage I was offered the chance to do a PhD. I had the choice of three similar areas and an afternoon to make up my mind. I spent that afternoon finding out all I could about each subject, and ended up studying for a PhD in neutron scattering studies of disorder, which meant looking at the way the atoms are arranged inside some disordered crystalline materials. It was a good choice because I enjoyed nearly every minute of it. Although my PhD involved looking at a traditional problem, I did so using very novel computational techniques which were only developed the year before I started my research. I finished my PhD in less than three years: I worked very hard and was well organised. I published a number of papers as I went along and this helped me to write up on time.

I then obtained a three-year EPSRC postdoctoral fellowship at the University of Birmingham to work on the structure of ice. My interview at Birmingham was a result of a personal recommendation – networking, in other words – and I was the only person interviewed for the position.

The disadvantages of short-term contracts are obvious: you never really feel settled because you're scared about what's going to happen next. But there are advantages too. I think a postdoc can teach you to be more independent and you can acquire a lot of different experience by working with new sets of people, especially if you change universities between contracts. It's essential to use a short-term contract positively: you have to make things happen for yourself. I took advantage of any opportunities that were offered to me, especially conferences and meetings. I made sure I published many papers, worked long hours at my research, and 'infiltrated' the networks whenever possible.

A postdoc is not a 9 to 5 job: you need to be really dedicated. When an opportunity came up to use somebody else's experimental rig, I spent a whole Easter weekend working on it, gaining data for my project and, more importantly, expertise in a different research field.

During the second year of my short-term contract I was advised to start thinking about applying for an EPSRC or Royal Society five-year advanced fellowship, but I didn't think I was good enough. I decided that as I had had only had one interview in recent years, I needed some interview practice to find out what everybody wanted and which skills and areas of knowledge I needed to develop. Towards the end of my second year I therefore applied for some lectureships to get interview experience, and succeeded in obtaining my current position at the University of Kent!

The first year here was a little chaotic: I felt I was running around in circles and achieving very little in terms of research or teaching. Happily I sorted out my priorities in my second year and I now feel I am on top of the job.

I enjoy the balance of research and teaching. My research work focuses on developing new refinement techniques for crystallographic data and I find this very absorbing, but I also like the contact with other people that teaching involves, and the challenge of putting ideas across. That's one reason why I volunteered to become the Department's schools liaison officer, visiting schools and organising events for pupils and teachers. That role takes up a fair amount of time but I believe it is worthwhile. Because I'm a woman in physics I am seen as a positive role model for girls, but I also think it is important for boys, too, to see that girls can do a job like mine.

Further information

If you are currently completing your PhD, your supervisor or mentor should point you in the right direction for further information on postdoctoral positions such as those funded by The Royal Society and The Wellcome Trust. Your colleagues within the university may also be able to provide you with useful advice and addresses of particularly relevant Internet sources. Several grant-awarding bodies offer other types of funding such as that designed to get people back into research after a career break. Some of these are discussed in more detail on pages 133-34.

The Research Councils fund postgraduate study with various scholarships, studentships, fellowships and awards. You can find out more about application procedures, approved courses and terms and conditions of service from your university or from the Research Councils directly at the addresses listed below.

Biotechnology and Biological Sciences Research Council (BBSRC)
Polaris House
North Star Avenue
Swindon
SN2 1UH
Tel: 01793 413 200; fax: 01793 413 201; website: http://www.bbsrc.ac.uk

Council for the Central Laboratory of the Research Councils (CCLRC)
Rutherford Appleton Laboratory
Chilton
Didcot
Oxfordshire
OX11 1QX
Tel: 01235 445 475; fax: 01235 445 584; website http://www.cclrc.ac.uk

Engineering and Physical Sciences Research Council (EPSRC)
Polaris House
North Star Avenue
Swindon
SN2 1ET
Tel: 01793 444 000; fax: 01793 444 010; website: http://www.epsrc.ac.uk

Natural Environment Research Council (NERC)
Polaris House
North Star Avenue
Swindon
SN1 1DE
Tel: 01793 411 500; fax: 01793 411 501; website: http://www.nerc.ac.uk

Particle Physics and Astronomy Research Council (PPARC)
Polaris House
North Star Avenue
Swindon
SN2 1SZ
Tel: 01793 442 000; fax: 01793 442 106; website: http://www.pparc.ac.uk

Medical Research Council (MRC)
20 Park Crescent
London
W1N 4AL
Tel: 0171 636 5422; fax: 0171 636 6179; website: http://www.mrc.ac.uk

Association of Medical Research Charities (AMRC)
29–35 Farringdon Road
London
EC1M 3JB
Tel: 0171 404 6454; fax: 0171 404 6448; email: amrc@mailbox.ulcc.ac.uk

An umbrella organisation for nearly 90 charities, the AMRC provides general information about member charities and publishes an annual handbook with contact details for those who wish to apply for grants from member organisations. It does not act as an agent in the processing of research applications. Handbook available on website: http://www.amrc.org.uk, where the pages are continually updated.

Other research projects and grants can be 'mission driven', focusing on particular problems. Consequently other sources of funding can include business, charities, industry, Government departments and the EC, sometimes directly and sometimes through the Research Councils.

Dorothy Hodgkin Fellowships

The Dorothy Hodgkin Fellowships are offered by the Royal Society and provide high-level support and flexibility designed to encourage women into – and to stay in – research. Contact:

Royal Society Research Fellowships
Research Appointments Department
6 Carlton House Terrace
London
SW1Y 5AG
Tel: 0171 451 2547; fax: 0171 930 2170;
website: http://www.royalsoc.ac.uk./rs/
email: ukresearch.appointments@royalsoc.ac.uk

The following two publications should be obtainable via your university library or from HMSO.

House of Lords Select Committee on Science and Technology, Academic Research Careers for Graduate Scientists Report

July 1995, HMSO, HL Paper 60 (The 'Dainton Report')

This generally highlighted the problems of short-term contracts and suggested various steps to remedy the situation.

House of Lords Select Committee on Science and Technology, Academic Research Careers for Graduate Scientists Evidence

1994, HMSO, HL Paper 60–1

Very long, but fascinating reading, particularly the consistency of the arguments detailing the problems of short-term contracts, and as an insight into the way Government committees work.

A Concordat on Contract Research Staff Career Management

The Royal Society, The British Academy, BBSRC, EPSRC, ESRC, MRC, NERC, PPARC, CVCP, SCOP, COSHEP, 1996

The full details of the recommendations of the above bodies to provide a framework for the career management of contract research staff in universities and colleges. Available on website: http://www.cvcp.ac.uk

The Association of University Teachers (AUT) publishes a booklet outlining good employment practice, and reports on contract research staff matters in its regular publications.

Contact:
The AUT
United House
9 Pembridge Road
London W11 3JY
Tel: 0171 221 4370; fax: 0171 727 6547; website: http://www.aut.org.uk
email: hq@aut.org.uk

8

All change? branching out

'My first boss said: "Keep moving. It's more difficult to hit a moving target." And I followed his advice. I moved from industry to academia and back again six times. I made that possible by always working at the interface between the two sectors. I've thrived on change and it's benefitted my career.' Professor of biophysics/managing director of a biotechnology company

An SET qualification has to be the smart option. The Association of Graduate Recruiters (AGR) argues that there is an increasing demand for and acceptance of science subjects in areas not directly concerned with science, engineering and technology, and therefore more scope for graduates to switch after university if that is appropriate. Consequently if, as estimated, over 52% of jobs are open to graduates with any degrees, people who also have the option of choosing a specific career in SET must have one of the widest choices of all. Having said that, as Chapter 3 points out, getting a job – and especially getting a good job – is still a tough challenge, and within SET certain areas are highly competitive.

If you do study for a qualification in SET – or even if you pursue an SET-related career for a number of years – this does not necessarily mean that you will spend the rest of your life in SET. The expertise you acquire, and the skills you develop through the rigorous discipline of SET can be easily transferable, whether you want to go into the City, into the media, into management, into local government or into something completely different.

Today SET graduates and people with SET skills are considered to be highly employable as they will probably have developed a considerable range of competences such as:

- an in-depth knowledge of one or more specific areas of SET and the ability to apply that expertise in different sectors
- an understanding of technical issues
- numeracy
- computer literacy and advanced IT skills
- strong technical writing abilities
- the ability to think analytically
- problem-solving skills
- business and interpersonal skills such as teamworking and leadership
- both oral and written communication skills.

While there are no guarantees, the broader and stronger your skills base, the more likely it is that you will be employable for more of the time, in a wider range of areas and at a higher salary level. A strong portfolio of SET skills and knowledge will give you that critical edge in many job markets.

All change?

- Perhaps you have enjoyed working in SET for some years but are now ready for a change.
- Perhaps your family or geographical limitations mean that you are unable to work in SET.
- Perhaps you are about to graduate with an SET degree and feel that a 'straightforward' career in SET is not for you.
- Or perhaps you feel you have come to a 'dead-end' and now need a different challenge.

Whatever the reason, if you are unhappy in your present work situation, this will inevitably have repercussions in many other areas of your life apart from your job, and it will certainly not advance your career. At the right time, even an enforced career change can be a real opportunity. After all, a change is not always as good as a rest. Sometimes it can be much better.

So, where do you go next?

There are no right or wrong paths, no right or wrong decisions: the important thing is to work out on balance what you really want to do and then go for it.

What have other people done? Here are some career profiles to illustrate just some of the possibilities. These routes are not all-encompassing, but are intended to suggest some of the vast range of options open to you, and to indicate how other women have tackled the difficult task of deciding what they wanted to do with their lives.

'Trained scientists and engineers may move into other fields such as industrial management, school teaching, journalism or public administration. In these circumstances their education and training enables them to bring to their work an understanding of the positive contribution which SET can make to wealth creation and the quality of life.' The Rising Tide, 1994, page 2

Perhaps you could be a PUBLISHER?

Dr Cathy Kennedy is the senior commissioning editor in biology at Oxford University Press (OUP). She is in her early 40s.

After gaining a degree in Psychology, and having done the research for my PhD in Animal Behaviour, I moved to Oxford with my partner where I worked in the Department of Zoology for 12 years. Initially I was working for nothing and writing up my thesis, but being in the Department gave me a library card, access to the amazing facilities, and enabled me to get my work known. The gamble paid off: five years of short-term research grants followed, and then six years as a demonstrator where I also gained teaching and tutoring experience. My particular interest was insect–plant relations: 'the host discrimination behaviour of the aphid' – in other words, how the aphid finds its food.

Children, short-term contracts and other issues caused me to review my career direction as I approached 40. Initially I focused on publishing: I could write a decent grammatical style, I could spell and edit, and I thought publishing would allow me to keep in touch with biology. However I was sidetracked by being offered a three-day-a-week job researching into different types of energy sources. Frustratingly this came to nothing and I was forced to resort to a short spell temping as a secretary in order to pay my nanny, before I went back to my original idea and responded to an advert for an in-house editor (in the Division of Science and Medicine) at OUP.

With no publishing experience, I got the job by the skin of my teeth and I had to take a substantial pay drop and go full-time in order to get a foot in the publishing door. But it seemed worth it. My view of publishing then was very limited; I think I assumed that once in, the progression to commissioning books in one's own subject was a natural one.

The role of an in-house editor is a co-ordinating one, managing the whole publishing process, dealing with all the different publishing departments and liaising with the author, making sure that things happen in the right place at the right time. Training is usually on the job – you pick it up as you go along, taking advice from your colleagues.

There was plenty to learn, though after three years I was starting to get bored. Serendipity played its part: a senior publisher retired, there was a change in management and I became a commissioning editor for whole organism biology. This involves finding where books are needed, striving to find authors for them, evaluating the proposals and typescripts that we receive, submitting costings and looking after an extensive backlist.

I am now the senior editor responsible for a diverse biology list ranging from forestry and veterinary science to marine biology, ornithology, animal behaviour, evolution and ecology. As much of the work involves reading scientific papers, going to conferences and visiting authors and universities, my time spent as a research scientist has been hugely useful. It gives me credibility. Authors accept that I talk the same language and they visibly relax when they learn I've got a PhD. Strategic thinking is important to retain focus, and I have a heavy workload with a backlist of several hundred titles, 80 books between contract stage and final manuscript, and 20 in production.

This is a demanding job but I enjoy it tremendously. The most difficult part is trying to achieve the right balance with family life. Frequent travel means long hours or up to a whole week away at a time, and the job itself could easily occupy every spare moment. For me it's possible because my partner is self-employed and works from home, so with frequent comparing of calendars and by working slightly out of phase we can manage the childcare.

Although there are publishing degrees, a science or medical degree is equally – or in some cases more – useful. Get what experience you can, even if it means photocopying typescripts in a publisher's office for little or no money. Get your face known, find out about all aspects of the publishing process, be alert to opportunities – and persevere.

Factfile

Have you got what it takes to be a publisher?

Within the last decade publishing has become very technology-based, and so women with skills in information technology and science are in a good position to work in this field. Any experience such as working on a student newsletter or student magazine will help you.

To be a copy editor, production editor or in-house editor you will need:

- good communication skills
- tact
- an eye for detail
- organisational skills
- keyboard and word-processing skills
- good spelling and writing style.

To be a commissioning or managing editor you will need:

- training in and an extensive knowledge of the area in which you are commissioning
- sound judgement and an ability to formulate strategy
- entrepreneurial skills
- the ability to work in a competitive business environment.

Are professional qualifications necessary?

There are various university and college courses in publishing, and you can do an NVQ in Book Editing (Editorial Management) at Level 4 with the Open University (OU). Most copy editors will have a degree and nearly all commissioning editors a higher degree in a relevant subject.

Professional bodies

The Publishers Association
1 Kingsway
London WC2B 6XF
Tel: 0171 565 7474; fax: 0171 836 4543; email: @publishers.org.uk

Book House Training Centre
45 East Hill
Wandsworth
London SW18 2QZ
Tel: 0181 874 2718; fax: 0181 870 8985;
website: http://www.zynet.co.uk./ethos/contacts/bhtc; email: bhtc@dial.pipex.com

Women in Publishing
c/o 12 Dyott Street
London
WC1A 1DF

Further reading

Books: The Culture and Commerce of Publishing
Lewis A. Coser *et al.*, The University of Chicago Press, 1985

Still one of the best overviews of traditional publishing, although it is written from an American standpoint and predates the extensive introduction of computer technology into writing and publishing.

The Bookseller

This weekly magazine, quaintly subtitled 'The organ of the book trade', covers news and current issues in publishing and bookselling, and advertises job openings in all aspects of these fields.

Basic Editing, a practical course. The Text
and
Basic Editing, a practical course. The Exercises
Nicola Harris, Book House Training Centre, 1991

A very useful course that you can work through by yourself; it provides some of the information and can enable you to develop some of the skills you will need as an editor.

Copy-editing
Judith Butcher, Cambridge University Press, 3rd edition 1992

The copy editor's bible.

Book Commissioning and Acquisition
Gill Davies, Blueprint, 1995

An excellent introduction to commissioning in all areas of book publishing.

Family-friendly?

Some positions lend themselves to part-time work and flexible hours. Many copy editors and indexers work on a freelance basis. However, commissioning editors have a highly demanding and sometimes stressful role, and will be expected to travel frequently.

The growing number of scientific and academic journals is another publishing area which you might usefully wish to investigate. For another view of publishing – and in particular how it can fit in with family life – see the profile of Jane Holland, managing editor of the *Geological Magazine*, on page 94.

Perhaps you could be a PATENT AGENT?

Clare Matthews is in her early 40s. Like many patent agents, she works in a private practice, although patent agents may be employed by large industrial companies in a patent department. A few patent agents are employed by firms of solicitors and work alongside solicitors specialising in intellectual property law.

After two years reading Natural Sciences I knew I wanted a change. I enjoyed science, but no longer wanted to deal exclusively with it; however I would not have been happy in a less rigorous environment and so law, with its logical structure, seemed the best option for me. Consequently I read law during the final year of my degree.

I didn't fancy becoming an accountant, a tax inspector or a perfume chemist (those being the helpful suggestions of the University Careers Service) but when becoming a patent agent was suggested, the fusion of law and science immediately appealed. A subsequent chat with a patent agent confirmed it would fit both my academic background and my interests and skills.

Even then it was hard to get a job; now it is far more so: there are so many extremely able, well-qualified people wanting to enter the field. I sent off about 30 applications, had seven interviews and only one job offer which I obviously accepted. Today you are more likely to have to send off up to a 100 applications and the only advice I can give to anybody wishing to become a patent agent is to keep on trying. I would say, however, that it makes no difference whether you are a woman or a man – you are judged on your qualifications and abilities.

Training then was – and still is – largely an 'apprenticeship': you learn on the job, which nowadays can be supplemented by some academic courses at Queen Mary and Westfield College, such as that leading to the Certificate of Intellectual Property Law. There are several exams you need to take and these take a minimum of three years – and often considerably longer.

The demanding nature of the training reflects the demanding nature of the job. After 21 years I'm still learning on all fronts. Not only is the law constantly changing as new acts are introduced and judicial and Patent Office decisions are made, but the nature of the subject matter also means that you have to keep up with the latest scientific and technological information on a relentless basis, particularly in areas such as microbiology and biotechnology.

One of the aspects I enjoy about being a patent agent is making order out of chaos. The job involves collecting, assimilating and analysing masses of information and putting it down on paper so that an invention is both described and defined. I enjoy the intellectual challenges of the subject matter. There's immense and unpredictable pressure at times and the business is beset by deadlines. There's lots of hard graft, you have to see something through to the bitter end through the tedious stages, and you can't afford to let your concentration slip: one small mistake could jeopardise everything. I frequently agonise over individual words – it helps to be pedantic by nature! Thousand of pounds can hinge on a single word or phrase.

It's not all office based however: there's lots of scope for visiting clients, and I enjoy the fascination of dealing with inventors, and working with the research and inventions which might change our daily lives. I have been involved with a wide range of topics including antibody engineering, AIDS research, immunoassays, tea manufacture, rotary motion drives, poultry handling, vehicle body assembly equipment, electrophoretic techniques, fragrances, electrochemical biosensors, salami manufacture and dental cement – to name but a few!

It's a reasonably 'family-friendly' profession: agents can work part-time and a few work from home as the work consists of self-contained jobs. The other reason it's possible to work outside an office is that despite all the inventions, the basic tools of the patent agent's trade are the very simplest: a pen and paper.

Factfile

Have you got what it takes to be a patent agent?

- a degree in a scientific or technical discipline is almost essential
- a detailed knowledge of intellectual property law acquired through training
- an analytical mind
- sound practical sense
- an eye for detail
- excellent communication skills

Are professional qualifications necessary?

Yes, if you want to qualify as a Chartered Patent Agent and also as a European Patent Attorney. As well as examinations leading to entry on the UK Register of Patent Agents and the UK Register of Trade Mark Agents, nowadays all trainees aim to pass the European Qualifying Examination, which makes it extremely difficult (but not impossible) to qualify without a technical/scientific degree.

Professional body

Chartered Institute of Patent Agents
Staple Inn Buildings
High Holborn
London
WC1V 7PZ
Tel: 0171 405 9450; fax: 0171 430 0471; website: http://www. cipa.org.uk/cipa

Further reading

The Ivanhoe Guide to Chartered Patent Agents

Clear and up-to-date information written by people inside the profession. Published annually by Cambridge Market Intelligence Ltd (tel: 0171 924 7117; fax: 0171 403 6729).

Family-friendly?

The profession is well paid, so quality childcare is an affordable option, and you can work from home and part-time. However, career breaks can be difficult as the practices are often small and the other members of the practice can't always carry your workload.

Perhaps you could be a MEMBER OF PARLIAMENT?

Anne Campbell is the current MP for Cambridge. With a degree in mathematics, and a background in teaching, lecturing, statistics and information technology, she was first elected to Parliament in 1992. Anne Campbell is in her 50s and has three children and three grandchildren.

I think the pattern of changes in my career is one that is increasingly common today. In my case, whether or not to make the transition has always been a difficult decision because I very much enjoyed the job that I was already doing.

My 'first' career was in education: I started as a teacher of mathematics in a secondary school, and eventually became a senior lecturer in statistics at Anglia Polytechnic University. I had one career break and taught part-time for certain periods as I was raising my family; this was relatively easy for me to do as mathematics teachers were in such demand.

In order to keep up to date, I also studied for a professional qualification in statistics and this led indirectly to my first change of career in my early 40s when I became head of statistics and data processing at the National Institute of Agricultural Botany (NIAB). I heard about the job through a Statistics Discussion Group I was attending – a good example of networking! The work at NIAB was fascinating: it gave me a chance to put my knowledge of statistics into practice and it took me into computing. I also learned a great deal about Government departments and the Civil Service, and travelled all over Europe.

I hadn't planned to become an MP. It came about through a long series of events that started with my involvement in the Parent Teacher Association (PTA) at my children's school. From there I chaired the Cambridgeshire Inter–PTA which was fighting cuts in education. I discovered I liked campaigning and whilst I was working at NIAB I became a county councillor to see what changes I could make from the 'other side of the fence'. After four years on the Council, I was looking forward to some time to myself, only to discover my name had been put on to the selection list for Parliamentary candidates.

I wasn't sure I wanted to become an MP and nearly removed my name from the list. In the end I won the selection 'by my fingernails' with 0.2% of the vote: I think that the Party was looking for someone 'a bit different' and being a woman and a scientist usually fits that criterion! Having a background like mine is also useful in a place like Cambridge which has a strong scientific/IT base in research, education and industry.

In 1992 I was fighting for the seat from the third position and I thought Labour would win the election and the Conservatives would win Cambridge; in the event, the exact opposite occurred. It was an amazing feeling to be elected: I was completely overwhelmed. One of the best things was that my son had his 18th birthday some weeks before, and he was able to cast his first vote – for me!

As an MP, there is no pre-defined role. I knew I wanted to be a strong constituency MP, and also to direct some of my energies towards scientific issues. On the science side, I was appointed to the House of Commons Select Committee on Science and Technology where the work included a report on global climate change and a review of public sector research establishments. I then chaired the Parliamentary and Scientific Committee for two years, which is the oldest of the Backbench committees. I have also made a contribution in other areas such as the role of IT in education, the proposed University for Industry, and with groups working at the interface between science and politics.

In 1997 I was returned with a majority of 14,137, and was appointed as Parliamentary Private Secretary to the Minister for Science, Energy and Industry. This utilises my previous experience in science policy making and I am enjoying it immensely.

One of the things I most enjoy about being an MP is that it allows me to express both sides of my personality: at one end of the spectrum I am involved with individual people, such as making sure that a war pensioner gets some special spectacles, and at the other with organisations and public policy, as with the debate about cloning. As an MP you are in a powerful position and you can make such a difference to some people's lives. The first time I walked into the House of Commons, I thought 'Wow!' Five years on, I still get that feeling.

Factfile

Have you got what it takes to be an MP?

- a genuine concern about and commitment to specific issues
- excellent communication skills
- perseverance
- the ability to withstand criticism and rejections

Are professional qualifications necessary?

No. However you will need to get involved with the political party of your choice and make sure that you know how it works.

Professional bodies

The political parties

Emily's List gives grants to women in the Labour party seeking selection.
Emily's List
P O Box 708
London SW10 0DH
Tel: 01666 577 955

The 300 Group – see page 199

Family-friendly?

No – for neither men nor women! Many MPs become 'weekend parents', especially if their constituency is distant from London.

Perhaps you could be a LAWYER?

Zoë Keene is in her early 20s. After graduating with a BSc in Biochemistry, she is now studying to be a solicitor.

'You must be a scientist,' my tutor said as she handed me back the first assignment I'd done on my law conversion course. 'It shows. You have a different way of looking at things and your approach is far more succinct.'

When I finished my university course I didn't know which way to go. I couldn't see myself either doing research or working in a lab and so I decided to use my degree as a general starting point and went into selling agricultural feeds. It wasn't me – I loved being out and about and meeting the farmers and having a cup of tea with them, but I wasn't much good at selling.

Law had always fascinated me: I shared a house with a law student at university and read many of her books, and I enjoy dealing with people and their problems, and so I decided to apply to law school. I've completed the one year full-time law conversion course leading to the Common Professional Examination (CPE) and I'm currently studying for my solicitor's finals.

I think law is completely different from science but, as my tutor had recognised, I found the systematic way of thinking that studying science fosters very useful when analysing legal information and problems. The other thing I noticed was that having studied mathematics to a certain level, I wasn't scared of numbers. Most of the other students – and even some of the lecturers! – seemed petrified by tax law, for instance. For me the number crunching was simple stuff.

I'm now in the process of applying for articles and I'm intending to get some work experience with a firm of solicitors in Liverpool that specialise in work-related diseases. That area of law or medical negligence would be a logical choice for me with my degree in biochemistry so I thought I'd see what it's like. On the other hand, I might opt for criminal law. I'm not sure yet.

I didn't really want to go back to being a student – I'm working all hours and paying out a fortune for the privilege. My friends are all earning, and sometimes I wonder if I'm doing the right thing. But I know that once I'm qualified there'll be so many options open to me, and at the end of the day it's doing something that you enjoy that counts.

Factfile

Have you got what it takes to be a lawyer?

- excellent communication skills
- good presentation skills
- an eye for detail
- negotiating skills
- a good memory
- the ability to concentrate on several things at once
- steady nerves

Are professional qualifications necessary?

Yes, the Common Professional Examination (CPE) or Postgraduate Diploma in Law are essential, which, if you have a degree other than law, take one year full-time or two years part-time.

Then, if you want to be a solicitor, you must do a one-year full-time or two-year part-time Legal Practice Course, followed by another two years on a Training Contract during which time you have to complete the Professional Skills Course.

If you want to be a barrister, after the one-year conversion course, you will need to complete the one-year Bar Vocational Course, and then you will have to do a year's pupillage working with a barrister in a set of chambers gaining on-the-job experience. Following pupillage, there is a compulsory system of Continuing Professional Development for three years.

Professional bodies

The Council of Legal Education, The Law Society, is responsible for solicitors' training. There is also an Association of Women Solicitors, contactable at the Law Society. Find out more from:

The Law Society
113 Chancery Lane
London WC2A 1PL
Tel: 0171 242 1222; fax: 0171 831 0344

The General Council of the Bar of England and Wales is responsible for barristers' training. Find out more from:

The General Council of the Bar
Academic Stage Section
2/3 Cursitor Street
London
EC4A 1NE
Tel: 0171 440 4000; fax: 0171 440 4002

Further reading

The Ivanhoe Guide to the Legal Profession

Clear and up-to-date information written by people inside the profession. Published annually by Cambridge Market Intelligence Ltd (tel: 0171 924 7117; fax: 0171 403 6729).

Perhaps you could be a TEACHER?

Dr Katharine Krebs is head of biology at a secondary school. She is now in her early 50s and has been in teaching for 15 years.

Teaching was never a second choice for me. I've always wanted to teach, but after I obtained my first degree (in Zoology) I wondered about obtaining some additional experience first. When I was offered the opportunity to do a research degree, I asked the Department of Education for guidance. They pointed out that the research experience would be useful, and that I could enter teaching afterwards, but it would be more difficult to do it the other way round. As a result I did a DPhil in which I applied ethological techniques to study the behaviour of young children. That gave me a useful insight into research and investigative techniques, and into ways of using statistical knowledge.

My DPhil was interrupted when I followed my husband to British Columbia, but I was able to complete it there, and I also taught practicals to first-year university students. When we returned to the UK, I decided to do a teacher training course even though I already had some teaching experience, as it would introduce me to a range of approaches, techniques and textbooks, suggest different ways of approaching planning lessons and syllabus interpretation, and give me practical experience of teaching different ages and different abilities. I therefore studied for a Postgraduate Certificate of Education (PGCE) at Bangor.

Once qualified, I taught in a comprehensive school in Thame. I wanted to teach 11–18 year olds because that meant I could use my subject in some depth at A-level, but I also appreciated the enthusiasm of the younger children: the way they bounce into the classroom is so very refreshing! Later on I took a career break when I had children, but did some coaching for a tutorial college. When my first daughter started school I became a parent governor. I went back to teach part-time when my younger daughter was four, and eventually became a full-time teacher again. At one stage I thought about applying for deputy headships but eventually decided against it as I felt that it would interfere with my other commitments and interests.

If you're thinking about being a teacher I would suggest you visit a variety of schools and sit in on lessons. I also think it's important to do something between graduating and teaching, and to keep a life and a network outside school: I have contacts with other schools and with the Education Committee of the Association for the Study of Animal Behaviour, all of which help to keep my interest in and knowledge of science up-to-date and relevant.

As a teacher you are in a powerful position, and you mustn't abuse that power. For instance, I use humour to cajole, but never to laugh at my pupils. In the past, like everybody, I've made a few mistakes: one group of 'challenging' 15-year-old girls drove me to despair and nearly to resignation, but I survived and they taught me a lot about teaching. I knew I was winning when I went into the classroom one day and informed them that as they didn't want to learn, I would just sit there and read. After 15 minutes of initial jubilation, one of the girls finally turned to me and said 'This is silly miss. You're supposed to be teaching us.' I wouldn't say it was plain sailing from then on, but at least we managed to make progress.

Teaching's great fun but there are drawbacks to the profession: it's getting harder with regular changes in the syllabus (which are sometimes difficult to interpret) and a heavier load of examination marking. I hate marking – it's repetitious but useful. If most of the class get it wrong, you know you haven't taught it properly.

I've been a teacher in several schools and in each one I've learned something new. There is a huge pleasure in working with young people – it's a privilege. I enjoy teaching biology because it is very rewarding and appeals to different pupils at different levels, and I also enjoy the creative side of planning lessons in a good school where science is appreciated. There are eleven girls in my current A-level group. Four are going on to do a degree in biology, and six in biologically related topics, so they must be enjoying it and will go on to make their own contribution. I find that very satisfying.

Factfile

Have you got what it takes to be a teacher?

- understanding and sympathy for children and young people
- excellent communication skills
- organisational skills
- confidence and imagination
- patience and a sense of humour
- a passion for your subject

Are professional qualifications necessary?

If you want to teach in a state maintained school you will need Qualified Teacher Status (QTS) which can be obtained by taking a course of initial teacher training (ITT). If you already have a degree or equivalent you can gain QTS by completing a one-year postgraduate course – normally for a Postgraduate Certificate of Education (PGCE). Alternatively you can gain QTS by completing a Bachelor of Education (BEd), or a BA or BSc with QTS.

(In independent schools and tutorial colleges a teaching qualification is usually desirable, sometimes essential.)

The Open University (OU – see page 132) offers a distance learning 18-month PGCE course.

There is also a Licensed Teacher Scheme (employment-based training) and School-Centred Initial Teacher Training (a full-time one year scheme for postgraduates only).

If you are planning to teach science (physics, chemistry or biology), mathematics, design and technology, or information technology, additional funding and other support might be available through the Priority Subject Recruitment Scheme. This could include funding industrial attachments, or extra money for students with dependants or previous relevant experience.

Find out more about the routes into teaching and the Priority Subject Recruitment Scheme from:

Teacher Training Agency
Communication Centre
PO Box 3210
Chelmsford
Essex
CM1 3WA
Tel: 01245 454 454; fax: 01245 261 668;
website: http://www.teach.org.uk;
email: teaching@ttainfo.demon.co.uk

Professional bodies

The Association for Science Education
College Lane
Hatfield
Herts
AL10 9AA
Tel: 01707 267 411; fax: 01707 266 532;
website: http://www.rmplc.co.uk/orgs/asehq/index.html;
email: ase@asehq.tellme.com

Teaching unions such as:
NUT (National Union of Teachers)
Hamilton House
Mabledon Place
London
WC1H 9BD
Tel: 0171 388 6191; fax: 0171 387 8458

NASUWT (National Association of Schoolmasters Union of Women Teachers)
Hillscourt Education Centre
Rose Hill
Birmingham
B45 8RS
Tel: 0121 453 6150; fax: 0121 457 6208

Family-friendly?

Yes (especially the holidays!) – but don't underestimate the amounts of marking and preparation you will have to do during the evenings, at weekends and in the vacations.

Perhaps you could be an ACCOUNTANT ...

Julie Deane is only in her late 20s but she has already obtained an honours degree in Natural Sciences from Cambridge, qualified as a chartered accountant, worked as a consultant in a computer consultancy in Chicago, and is now back at her old college as a development officer.

For as long as I could remember I'd wanted to be a research scientist so I was devastated when in my final year at university I discovered I didn't actually enjoy that type of work.

I panicked: what I was going to do? I felt very apologetic about not pursuing science as a career. After graduation, I went home to Swansea and read up about a lot of jobs. I found out more about the ones that interested me by visiting different offices and arranging to workshadow various people. Nobody was more amazed than me to find that accountancy really appealed: the range of work was varied with a great deal of client contact in many industries, and I liked the thought of working in a small and friendly office which was part of a multinational group (Coopers & Lybrand).

I joined Coopers & Lybrand as a trainee accountant. The training was very good but studying for the exams at the same time as working was hard, and I was relieved when I qualified as a chartered accountant. I realised that even in this completely different field, I was using many of the skills I'd acquired doing a science degree: in particular the ability to manage my time, prioritise and evaluate progress. Studying science also equips you with a whole way of thinking that you can carry into just about any aspect of your work and life afterwards.

Moreover, a scientific background helped my credibility with the different organisations I worked for. For instance, when I worked with a large brewery I could understand the brewing process and micro organisms involved, and I had a genuine interest in the way things worked.

Once qualified the flexibility of working for a multinational group soon became apparent when I followed my future husband to the USA. Accountancy is a truly international profession. I worked in the Chicago area for Coopers & Lybrand for three years. This involved long hours, high stress, extensive responsibility – and good pay. After a while, though, I started to want something different and that was when I joined a small 'start-up' computer consultancy ...

... or a **CONSULTANT** ...

Could I really leave a secure career job with a large multinational to work with a start-up computer consultancy with only 15 people? It was a fantastic opportunity but it was also a risk. My father used to suggest that when faced with a decision, I ask myself 'What's the worst thing that can happen?' So I did, and took the job.

My role as business manager offered me the chance to use my existing skills and expertise and develop new ones. It was much more creative and varied. The position was truly flexible, allowing me to combine financial management with computer consultancy. I learned more about IT, about dealing with clients, and about management skills. Most importantly, it showed me just how enjoyable work could be, and there was lots of room for me to grow with the company.

... or a **FUNDRAISING AND DEVELOPMENT OFFICER?**

The position of development officer advertised in my old college magazine coincided with my desire to return to England for family reasons. I applied for the job without too much optimism and was shocked to be shortlisted, and delighted when I was offered the job following a day of interviews.

As a development officer you build relationships with people and companies outside the institution in order to help it to enhance its strengths and secure its financial future. The primary focus is fundraising – for new buildings or student scholarships or teaching and research – but always with a view to the long-term vision of the College. The position of development officer was completely new, and I had to write a strategy for establishing a development office and a structure for an appeal, and then carry it forward. Although I used my accountancy skills for the financial aspects and my IT experience to set up a database, it was my scientific background which provided me with the know-how to set about such a big project in a disciplined and logical way. Coming up with ideas to raise money, developing them and carrying them out, and then evaluating the result as well as reaching a conclusion, is very much like designing an experiment and requires the same kind of discipline and objective method.

Many graduates look back on their days at College as some of the happiest of their lives. I am able to help such people re-establish a relationship in a way that is mutually beneficial.

If you're wondering about making a change, you might find it helpful to remember my father's advice. Just ask yourself 'What's the worst thing that can happen?' That simple question can be very liberating.

Factfile

Have you got what it takes to be an accountant?

- grasp of principles and practice of taxation and tax law
- excellent communication skills
- numeracy
- IT skills

Are professional qualifications necessary?

Yes: there are several different professional bodies who award various qualifications such as Chartered Accountant, Certified Accountant, or specialist accountant.

Professional bodies

Institute of Chartered Accountants in England and Wales (ICAEW)
Chartered Accountants Hall
P O Box 433
Moorgate Place
London
EC2P 2BJ
Tel: 0171 920 8677; fax: 0171 920 8603;
website: http://www.icaew.co.uk/menus/careers/baca.htm

Institute of Chartered Accountants in Scotland
27 Queen Street
Edinburgh
EH2 1LA
Tel: 0131 225 5673; fax: 0131 247 4872

The Association of Chartered Certified Accountants (ACCA)
Students' Promotion Department
29 Lincoln's Inn Field
London
WC2A 3EE
Tel: 0171 396 5800

The Chartered Institute of Taxation
12 Upper Belgrave Street
London
SW1A 8BB
Tel: 0171 235 9381; fax: 0171 235 2562

The Chartered Institute of Management Accountants (CIMA)
63 Portland Place
London W1N 4AB
Tel: 0171 637 2311; fax: 0171 631 5309

The Chartered Institute of Public Finance and Accountancy (CIPFA)
3 Robert Street
London WC2N 6BH
Tel: 0171 543 5600; fax: 0171 543 5700

Family-friendly?

Accountants are always in demand, and once qualified you should be able to practise full- or part-time, from an office or from home. Many firms now offer the option of job sharing.

Further reading

The Ivanhoe Guide to Chartered Accountants

Clear and up-to-date information written by people inside the profession. Published annually by Cambridge Market Intelligence Ltd (tel: 0171 924 7117; fax: 0171 403 6729).

Factfile

Have you got what it takes to be a computer consultant?

- excellent communication skills
- energy and enthusiasm
- expertise in IT

Family-friendly?

Consultancy can be a very demanding job, with long hours and extensive travel, but different firms have different requirements which should be discussed at the outset.

Factfile

Have you got what it takes to be a development officer/fundraiser?

- good contacts which will allow you to get through to the people who matter
- knowledge and familiarity with the overlapping worlds in which you are operating, for instance, education, business, industry or entertainment
- knowledge of potential sources of funding
- excellent communication skills
- energy and enthusiasm
- sincere and informed commitment to the cause

Are professional qualifications necessary?

No, although they help. The OU (see page 132) runs two courses aimed at people working in fundraising ('Managing voluntary and non-profit organizations' and 'Winning resources and support'), and the Institute of Charity Fundraising Managers runs a variety of courses.

Professional body

Institute of Charity Fundraising Managers
Market Towers
1 Nine Elms Lane
London SW8 5NQ
Tel: 0171 627 3436; fax: 0171 627 3508

Further reading

The Complete Fundraising Handbook
Sam Clarke, Directory of Social Change in association with the Institute of Charity Fundraising Managers, 2nd edition 1993

Charity Appeals: The complete guide to success
Marian Allford, J. M. Dent in association with the Institute of Charity Fundraising Managers, 1993

Relationship Fundraising
Ken Burnett, White Lion Press, 1995

Other information

Fundraising is a relatively new 'industry' in the UK and so it's a growth area where there are often insufficient people with the right experience to fill the positions advertised.

Perhaps you could be a NOVELIST?

Dr Ann Lackie/novelist Ann Lingard is now in her late 40s. She graduated with a BSc in Zoology, gained a PhD in Parasitology and held a research fellowship in Cambridge before moving to Scotland, where she taught at the University of Glasgow for 15 years. Then, in 1989 ...

After a lot of hard thinking, I decided I'd do the other thing I had always wanted to do in my life, to write fiction – so I opted for voluntary redundancy. I couldn't have made that decision if I hadn't had a husband who was willing to support me and our family while I 'started again', on the bottom rung of a new career. Even though I had written a lot, none of it had been fiction – so this career-change was a huge risk. And having given up my job and salary, I knew it was important to succeed!

The contrast between working in a busy lab, and working at home on one's own, is dramatic, but I was prepared for that and I actually rather enjoyed the prospect. And there are other important differences, too – in science, acquiring knowledge is a collaborative process, and 'creative' science moves forward from a sound basis of fact or at least high probability. Individuals 'create' hypotheses and design experiments, but then the results and ideas get discussed by the research group and at conferences. And, most important, good science is always recognised and the author of good science is acknowledged and the work respected.

In contrast, as a fiction-writer you're completely dependent on what comes out of your head! The creative process and its outcome are entirely due to your own imagination and ability to get the ideas into words. When you start, you don't know if what you are doing is any good, you can't put a 'probability value' on it. Also the people who read your work subsequently, whether agents or editors, rely on their own *subjective* judgement, on their own tastes. So – you have to recognise that this is all part of the game, and that it's also a game in which you must be prepared to shrug off rejections and carry on. Part of the folklore is that you 'paper the walls with rejection slips'!

I started with short stories, putting them in for various competitions, and also wrote non-fiction articles, and if anything was rejected I just sent it on to the next place on the list that I had drawn up. Two of my stories were eventually shortlisted in a prestigious writing competition, and that was a tremendous boost to my confidence, as I was then already well into my first novel.

I decided not to deal directly with publishers because I was too new to the game and didn't have any contacts, so eventually – getting an agent is almost as hard as finding a publisher! – I found an agent, and he very quickly obtained a two-book contract for me with HodderHeadline. I then discovered just how little I knew about the business of being an author – I thought that publication would be the end of the story, but I know now that an author has got to put in a lot of effort subsequently. You have to promote the book, make sure it's in the bookshops, try to use contacts to get the book reviewed. I read books about 'marketing books' to get some insights, and I now use a multifaceted approach to get my name remembered – I broadcast regularly on natural history on local radio, I write non-fiction articles for the local paper and for a wide range of magazines and journals, and I try to make sure I'm involved in 'writer's events' whenever possible.

It's hard work, but interesting, and sometimes it can be quite stressful. Ultimately though, I know I'm doing it for myself, and that if I want to succeed as a writer – and that means *earn a living*, not just write novels that are published but don't sell well – I have got to put in that effort.

My scientific background has undoubtedly helped. *Communicating* – ideas and enthusiasms, through the use of words and analogy, and through logical argument – is central to both writing fiction and lecturing about science. And discipline and perseverance are as important to a writer as to a research worker.

Do I miss science? If I allowed myself to look back, yes, I would miss the stimulus of doing research and being in the lab – but I can still read about science, and talk about science. And the business of writing is equally challenging and demanding. I actually think myself very fortunate to know what it is like to be a scientist *and* a fiction-writer.

'And what, then, of the courtship rituals? The student notices periods of verbal intercourse, when signals are exchanged; the interactions appear amicable and unexcited, but there are occasional outbursts of aggression, when the territorial conflict becomes dominant and the individuals separate and disperse. But, Harriet, think carefully: there were also occasions when the female, briefly, so very briefly but distinctly, reached out and touched the male. And did he not, once, briefly smooth the hair upon her head? Such small signals, subtle invitations, are at once noted and marked down and underlined by our invisible watcher, perhaps followed on the page by unscientific exclamation marks.' Ann Lingard, Figure in a Landscape, pages 186–7

Factfile

Have you got what it takes to be a writer?

- a keen eye for observation and a sharp ear for language
- imagination
- excellent communication skills
- keyboard skills
- perseverance
- ability to be alone for long periods
- a thick skin (for rejections and criticism) and a sensitive soul (to be able to write)
- an alternative source of income can be useful!

Are professional qualifications necessary?

No. However some universities now include creative writing in their degree courses.

Professional bodies

The Society of Authors
84 Drayton Gardens
London SW10 9SB
Tel: 0171 373 6642; fax: 0171 373 5768; email: authorsoc@writers.org.uk

The Society of Women Writers and Journalists
110 Whitehall Road
Chingford
London
E4 6DW
Tel: 0181 529 0886

Further information

Becoming a Writer
Dorothea Brande

This is a classic text and is available in several editions. It was first published in 1934 but has been reprinted many times since.

There are also a host of 'how to' books for the various writing genres. They can provide useful tips and 'shortcuts' – although they can't teach you how to write.

Bestseller
Olivia Goldsmith, HarperCollins, 1996

This provides an easy fictional insight into the possible ways of writing a bestseller. Chapters are preceded by clever quotes from the world of writing and publishing.

The Arvon Foundation (tel: 01409 231338) organises five-day residential courses run by various writers. Some people find the courses very inspiring and useful; others can be disappointed. It depends very much on whether the course is right for you.

There are many other weekend and short courses available run by various organisations – your local library might be able to supply you with further information.

Branching out

The above profiles describe just some of the many options that could be open to you. Women with SET qualifications are working as bankers and actuaries in financial organisations, as multimedia information librarians in major scientific companies, as public relations consultants for multinationals, and as development advisers for international charities. With experience of SET, you might want to work in a museum, in the armed services or in the media. Keep an open mind and don't reject possibilities until you have considered them.

But how do you go about branching out, if that is what you want to do?

You might find it useful to refer back to Chapter 1, and in particular the SWOT analysis and action plan. Then you could develop a new action plan along the following lines to focus on where you want to go next.

Action Plan: Getting out of your rut

Begin by LISTING:
- ❑ the reasons you want to change (more status? money? a sense of adventure?)
- ❑ the reasons you feel you should stay put (family commitments? financial restrictions? areas of satisfaction? timing?)
- ❑ what you want to achieve from moving in a new direction.

Then list the advantages and disadvantages of:
- ❑ staying put
- ❑ moving on.

Will your intended new career be compatible with your family commitments and desired lifestyle?

So you think you're ready for a change?

The first step is to ANALYSE:
- ❑ what you're good at
- ❑ what you enjoy about the job you're in
- ❑ what you dislike about the job you're in
- ❑ what skills and competences you've developed
- ❑ what you can bring to a job.

Next IDENTIFY:
- ❑ which sectors interest you
- ❑ which areas interest you
- ❑ which jobs interest you
- ❑ which direction you want to move in.

Then FIND OUT MORE:
- ❑ read up about specific jobs
- ❑ talk to people who are already working in those fields
- ❑ phone up the organisations that interest you and see if you can visit them
- ❑ make sure you know what it's really like
- ❑ analyse what the needs of the job are
- ❑ work out how your personality and abilities meet those needs.

Finally work out the WHEN? ...
- ❑ are you procrastinating, or being realistic?
- ❑ is it now or never?
- ❑ or can you use the present to make a smoother change in the future?

> **... and the HOW?**
> *Read Chapter 2 on further education and training (if appropriate), Chapter 3 on getting a job, and Chapter 4 on networking.* **Networking in particular is critically important if you are seeking a change of direction:** *who you know can make all the difference to your branching out successfully.*

- Perhaps the most important aspect of career planning is to realise what you enjoy doing.

- Don't be too influenced by your background.

- Pursue the opportunities that appeal to you and don't sell yourself short.

- Remember that for most people the decision itself to change career paths is often the hardest part, and that while you have to be realistic, it is possible to fulfil your dreams and ambitions. You owe it to yourself and your family to take some of the risks some of the time.

What Color is Your Parachute? by Richard Bolles (see page 185) uses extensive questionnaires, diagrams and checklists to help you work through the process of defining what you want to do with your life and in your career. It also outlines the best strategies to achieve your aims in great detail. You may find this book very useful – many people have: it was first published in 1970 and a new edition is published every year. Interestingly enough, the author has one degree in chemical engineering from the Massachusetts Institute of Technology and another in physics from Harvard!

In many ways the 'branching out' process can be like house-hunting. Once you start looking around, you may find that you begin to appreciate the benefits of what you've already got. On the other hand, considering other options may make you realise that it really is time to move on.

And if you do change direction and find it doesn't suit, don't be afraid to admit it and move on again.

Exploring other avenues

Perhaps you need a change, but are not ready or are unable to change your job completely. If this is your situation, you might want to investigate the following options:

- self-employment
- going abroad
- expanding your media activities
- taking up a public appointment.

The remainder of this chapter explores these alternative routes, but first it considers 'portfolio working' which can encompass some or all of these activities.

Portfolio working

One of the more resourceful ways of surviving – and thriving – is by becoming a portfolio worker. 'Portfolio working' is a term coined by the management guru Charles Handy to describe the way careers often develop. He argues: 'Rather than scurrying about looking for a corporate ladder to climb or a professional trajectory to follow, [people] ought to develop a product, skill or service, assemble a portfolio that illustrates these assets, and then go out and find customers for them.' Charles Handy, *Beyond Certainty: the changing world of organisations*, 1995, page 26

If you 'evolve' into a 'portfolio worker', you might divide your time between working for money, doing voluntary work, developing a particular hobby or interest, and enjoying your family. Portfolio working can have several advantages, not least of which is the space to develop your whole personality and different aspects of your life. It can also put you in a stronger and more interesting position, career-wise: 'A single fixed identity is a liability today. It only makes people more vulnerable to sudden changes in economic and personal conditions. The most successful and healthy amongst us now develop multiple identities, managed simultaneously and to be called upon as conditions change.' Gail Sheehy, *New Passages*, 1996, page 82

In some ways, portfolio working could be seen as the equivalent of political pluralism with many centres of power and expertise, but often it is not initially seen in a positive light. Frequently portfolio working seems not to be a genuine choice, but either develops or is thrust upon people. However, if you can develop an effective 'portfolio', you will probably find that you won't want to look back: 'I was devastated when my short-term contract researching into water soluble polymers wasn't renewed but looking back it was the best possible thing that could happen to me. I was forced to develop new skills and areas of expertise and now I am no longer dependent on a single area of work.' Chemist working in industry

Portfolio working encompasses most styles of working, including part-time employment, short-term contracts, voluntary work and running a home and a family. Frequently though, portfolio workers are self-employed ...

Self-employment

The number of self-employed people is growing and self-employment is a route that increasing numbers of women are taking, some through choice, others through lack of choice. Some people make a conscious decision to start their own business; others may choose this option when they move, or are made redundant. Many women find that self-employment can fit in with a certain stage of their lives, for instance, when they have a young family. This was Deborah Oppenheim's experience.

Dr Deborah Oppenheim, research biologist

Dr Deborah Oppenheim had worked in marine, estuarine and freshwater environments in a wide range of geographical areas. She started her own business when she was about to have her second baby. She is now in her mid 30s with two young children.

As I had a young baby to look after, I had logistical constraints on applying for jobs. Ten hours of technical interviews for different jobs made me realise I had expertise that I didn't want to lose. I decided to become a freelance algal consultant to the water industry. I was eight months pregnant when I formed my own company, Oppenheim Research Ltd, and the first thing I did as a director was to give myself maternity leave.

I enjoyed being freelance, liaising with so many different management and scientific levels in a business environment and doing demanding scientific work. However, a contraction in the job market in the areas in which I was working meant increased competition, which would have involved travelling all over the country. This defeated the original object of the exercise – one of the reasons I'd set up my company was because I didn't want to work away from home. The final problem was when I couldn't keep pace with new technology, either financially or in terms of training.

I don't regret working for myself though. I'd learned a lot, developed a whole new range of skills, increased my networks and kept my hand in whilst my children were young.

(After one year at home as a full-time mother and caring for her son who was ill, Deborah applied for a Daphne Jackson Fellowship partly in order to update her knowledge of technology. The subsequent development of her career is described on page 133.)

Self-employment is never an easy option, but it can be an exciting one. If you're thinking about working for yourself – and you have a choice – it might help to consider the following points:

- The stress and the pressure are unremitting: 'You are only as good as your last assignment and you can't afford to make any mistakes.' Self-employed civil engineer

- Self-employment is usually feast or famine: 'I had no work at all, and then everything came up at once and I was working evenings and weekends for months on end.' Telecommunications consultant

- Working from home all too often means an invasion of your home and your home life: 'It wasn't until I converted the loft into an office that I was able to cut off from my work. Now I can literally "shut the door on it". It feels as if I've got the house back.' Acoustic engineer

- Isolation can be a problem: 'It was very lonely, sitting at home and trying to chase up the next piece of work. In the end I set up a "Home alone" club just to get some social input.' Software designer

To be self-employed, you have to be a 'self-starter'. You have to be able to create and maintain an infrastructure for yourself or be sufficiently successful to employ others to do it for you. Unlike joining an existing organisation, you alone will be responsible for organising all the administration such as the bookkeeping and accounts, income tax and VAT payments, and for the provision of equipment, stationery and supplies. If you employ others, you will have to ensure that you fulfil all the health and safety requirements and so on. And after all that, you still have to make enough money to ensure that you can pay yourself a reasonable salary and make provision for a pension for your old age!

On the other hand, if you have a strong sense of independence, reasonable management and financial skills, good contacts and a sound business idea, self-employment has many advantages.

- There is a wonderful sense of freedom.
- The opportunity exists to work the hours that suit you when it suits you.
- Once established, you can pick and choose the work you do, your conditions of work and what you are paid.
- You have the privilege of really defining what you want to do with your time and your life.
- You can have a terrific sense of achievement.

With the 'patchwork-quilt' style of career, the pattern of moving in and out of self-employment as described by Deborah Oppenheim is not uncommon – it was also Maureen Donnelly's experience (see page 16). Self-employment can be a useful way of managing career breaks incurred for family, redundancy or locational reasons. Other women, like Sue Bird (see page 200), have found that the independence of running their own business is a longer-term attraction and many self-employed people would not contemplate working for an employer again, no matter what inducements were offered!

If self-employment is a route which you want to explore, some of the books listed on page 186 will be useful.

Thinking globally

Have you thought about going abroad for a spell? That could provide you with the sense of adventure for which you might be yearning. As well as working abroad, consider the possibility of studying abroad (see page 32), or working with a charity for a limited period.

More and more organisations value international experience and seek staff with the ability to operate within different cultures and societies. If you are ambitious and want to achieve a senior position, you will need to be able to demonstrate that you are at home in today's global working environment.

Working in SET you can have a truly international career, whether you work for a British organisation abroad or a foreign company or a multinational. In many fields of work and research, international collaboration is the norm. Companies and universities now often expect staff to participate in formal and informal visits and exchanges, international conferences, assignments, secondments or sabbaticals abroad.

If you come to a temporary 'full stop' in your career, it might be that time spent working, studying or researching abroad will give you added transferable skills that will equip you for promotion to a more senior level. This is worth bearing in mind early on in your career as it is useful to build up your international experience while you are relatively free of personal and family commitments. Again, the books listed in the Further Reading section will help you to find out more about this option.

If you do go abroad, remember to check out your income tax and pension situation before you go.

International Technology Service – Secondments

In an increasingly global market, UK companies face intense competition and need to be aware of technological developments and management practices from all over the world. In response to this challenge, the Department of Trade and Industry has established an International Technology Service, one of whose initiatives is to help smaller and medium-sized firms second members of their firms into world class companies overseas for periods of between three and 12 months. It is particularly directed towards firms with up to 2,000 employees and there is extra financial help available for firms with up to 250 staff. Contact:

International Technology Service – Secondments
The Project Office
Coopers & Lybrand
1 Embankment Place
London
WC2N 6NN
Tel: 0171 213 1851; fax: 0171 213 3075/2451; website: http://www.venus.co.uk/ibis

---

Sampling the other side

Perhaps you enjoy your work but feel you would like to reach a wider or different audience. If so, you might wish to consider expanding your 'media' activities. The Science and Technology Media Fellowships have been developed with the aim of communicating the importance of SET to the general public.

Science and Technology Media Fellowships

Up to ten media fellowships a year are offered to SET professionals by the British Association on behalf of COPUS (the Committee on the Public Understanding of Science – see page 190). The fellowships are designed to 'create greater awareness and understanding of the workings of the media among practising engineers and scientists' by providing opportunities for them to spend between four and eight weeks working with a newspaper or magazine, or in radio or television.

The fellowships are not intended for those who wish to enter the media, but to enable people in SET to communicate their science more effectively to the general public. Placements include programmes like BBC TV's *Tomorrow's World* and newspapers such as the *Financial Times* and the *Guardian*. For further information contact:

The British Association (MF)
23 Savile Row
London W1X 2NB
Tel: 0171 973 3500; fax: 0171 973 3051

Alternatively, the Royal Society/EPSRC/BBSRC Industry Fellowship Schemes can give you a taste of 'what you are missing'.

Royal Society/EPSRC/BBSRC Industry Fellowships Scheme

The primary objective of this scheme is to enhance communications between industry and universities or their equivalent, to the benefit of UK firms, higher education institutions and the individual scientist. It provides opportunities for post-doctoral employees in either sector to spend a period in the other sector.

For example, academic mathematicians, scientists or engineers can work in an industrial environment and undertake a project, while industrial scientists, mathematicians or engineers can undertake research or course-development work at a university. Arrangements for the fellowships are flexible. You can obtain further information from:

Research Appointments Department
The Royal Society
6 Carlton House Terrace
London
SW1Y 5AG

And finally ...

If you have family or financial commitments which make it difficult for you to have a complete change – or if you love your work and want to continue doing it but fancy developing in another direction – how about expanding your experience and interests by using your SET experience in a public appointment? The last chapter of this book describes what this might involve and how you can go about doing it.

A great deal of careers information is now available on the World Wide Web and the Internet, as well as in your local library or careers guidance office. The following books are recommended for further reading.

Considering a change?

What Color is Your Parachute? A practical manual for job hunters and career changers

Richard Nelson Bolles, Ten Speed Press, annually updated

One of the best books around on reviewing your career options, with exercises to work through and lots of good advice and sensible encouragement.

Assessing Your Career: time for change? Personal and professional development

Ben Ball, The British Psychological Society, 1996

Questionnaires and exercises designed to help you clarify your career ideas and assist in implementing change.

The Daily Telegraph Changing Your Job after 35

Geoffrey Golzen, Kogan Page, 7th edition 1993

Advice and information to help you implement the process of branching out.

Career ideas

The Penguin Careers Guide

Anna Alston and Anne Daniel (consultant editor: Ruth Miller), Penguin, 10th edition 1996

This book gives information on what different careers involve, and, interestingly, gives a summary of how well women are doing in each field.

Occupations

Judy Leavesley (editor), COIC (Careers and Occupational Information Centre), annually updated

This large format paperback is a detailed source of information on many different jobs. It should be available in your local library or careers guidance office.

The Careers Guide

Rosy Carter and Gail Eccles (editors), CASCaid/CRAC, annually updated

This paperback provides information on 650 jobs across all the work sectors at all levels.

Careers in Science and Engineering: a student planning guide to grad school and beyond

Committee on Science, Engineering and Public Policy, National Academy Press, 1996

(National Academy Press, 2101 Constitution Avenue, NW, Washington DC 20418)
This book is aimed at an American audience, but much of the information is also relevant to British women in SET who are trying to make educational and career choices, and the individual profiles are worth reading. This report is also available on the National Academy of Sciences' Internet host. It may be accessed via website: http://www.nas.edu.

Portfolio working

Beyond Certainty: the changing world of organisations

Charles Handy, Hutchinson, 1995

A thought-provoking mixture of essays, talks and articles about various aspects of the world in which we work. Charles Handy's other books are well worth reading, especially *The Age of Unreason* and *The Empty Raincoat*.

Self-employment

The WHICH? Guide to Starting Your Own Business: how to make a success of going it alone.

Consumers' Association, 1996

The Daily Telegraph Guide to Working for Yourself

Geoffrey Golzen, Kogan Page, 17th edition 1997

How to Set Up and Run Your Own Business

The Daily Telegraph, Kogan Page, 13th edition 1997

Lloyds Bank Small Business Guide

Sara Williams, Penguin, annually updated

Running a Home-Based Business

Diane M. Baker, Kogan Page, 1994

Starting a Technology Business

John Allen, Pitman in association with NatWest Technology Unit, 1992

Working abroad

The Daily Telegraph Guide to Working Abroad

Geoffrey Golzen, Kogan Page, 19th edition 1996

The Daily Telegraph Guide to Living Abroad

Michael Furnell and Philip Jones, Kogan Page, 10th edition 1997

'How to' series

There are a large number of books in the 'How to' series on getting a job abroad in many different countries. For further information contact How to Books, tel: 01752 202 301; fax: 01752 202 331.

9

Are we being heard? involvement in public life

'Women are still very poorly represented in senior appointments in both the public and private sector and on influential policy-making bodies.' The Rising Tide, 1994, page 3

In 1996 almost one third of all public appointments made by Government ministers were filled by women; this compared favourably with just under a quarter in 1991, and less than a fifth in 1986. Yet should this be a cause for congratulation when women make up over half the population? Many public bodies – and the decisions they make – could be described as 'male-oriented'.

This is especially true of SET-related appointments which reflect the minority representation of women in SET in general. Although steady progress is being made, even the 33% increase (between 1992 and 1995) in the number of women on the SET-related councils and boards as listed in *The Rising Tide*, still meant that the total representation was only 17%. Similarly, the proportion of women on the Research Council boards rose from 7.4% in 1992 to 13.5% in 1995, but there is obviously still a long way to go as the following table indicates.

Public appointments of men and women (M/F) to councils and boards in SET-related fields. Source: *Public Bodies 1992*, Cabinet Office, HMSO, 1993, and *Public Bodies 1995*, Cabinet Office, HMSO, 1996					
Non-departmental public bodies	**Parent department**	**1992**		**1995**	
		M/F	**%F**	**M/F**	**%F**
Royal Botanic Gardens	Ministry of Agriculture, Fisheries, & Food	9/3	25	9/3	25
National Food Survey Committee		4/1	20	6/1	17
Advisory Committee on Novel Foods & Processes		12/3	20	15/2	12
Defence Scientific Advisory Council & Committees	Ministry of Defence	156/2	1	149/5	3
Higher Education Funding Council for England	Department for Education & Employment	11/2	15	10/4	29
National Council for Educational Technology		11/8	42	8/6	43
National Council for Vocational Qualifications		12/0	0	12/2	14
Scottish Higher Education Funding Council	Scottish Office	10/2	17	12/3	20
Scottish National Heritage		11/1	8	10/2	17
Royal Botanic Garden Edinburgh		7/1	13	7/2	22

Cont'd over page

Non-departmental public bodies	Parent department	1992		1995	
		M/F	%F	M/F	%F
Higher Education Funding Council for Wales	Welsh Office	10/1	9	8/2	20
Welsh Medical Committee		19/2	9	20/2	9
Welsh Scientific Advisory Committee		14/1	7	12/3	20
Countryside Commission	Department of the Environment	6/2	25	7/2	22
Joint Nature Conservation Committee		4/0	0	2/1	33
Advisory Committee on Releases to the Environment		17/3	15	10/2	17
Building Regulations Advisory Committee		14/1	7	14/2	13
Royal Commission on Environmental Pollution		11/2	15	11/2	15
National Biological Standards Board	Department of Health	13/3	19	10/3	23
Public Health Laboratory Service Board		18/1	5	18/1	5
Human Fertilisation & Embryology Authority		10/11	52	9/11	55
Advisory Committee on NHS Drugs		11/4	27	15/5	25
Expert Advisory group on AIDS		15/6	29	12/6	33
Standing Pharmaceutical Advisory Committee		10/1	9	8/2	20
Museum of Science & Industry, Manchester	Department of National Heritage	12/3	20	10/4	29
Natural History Museum		11/2	15	9/3	25
National Museum of Science & Industry		14/3	18	6/5	45
Northern Ireland Council for Nature Conservation	Northern Ireland Office	12/8	40	12/28	40
Northern Ireland Building Regulations Advisory Committee		17/1	6	15/3	17
Northern Ireland Higher Education Council		8/3	27	9/3	25
Industrial Research & Technology Board		10/2	17	10/4	29

Non-departmental public bodies	Parent department	1992		1995	
		M/F	%F	M/F	%F
British Coal Corporation	Department of Trade & Industry	10/0	0	7/0	0
British Nuclear Fuels		11/1	8	10/2	17
United Kingdom Atomic Energy Authority		9/0	0	7/1	12
Renewable Energy Advisory Committee		14/1	7	16/3	16
Council for Science & Technology		11/1	8	11/1	8
Technology Foresight Steering Group		11/0	0	12/2	14
Research Councils (ex ESRC)		75/6	7	73/10	12
TOTAL		**641/92**	**13**	**601/123**	**17**

Why don't more women get involved in public life? Demanding careers, demanding families, a dislike of committees and experience of sexism, may all be factors which discourage women from 'stepping out'. And yet in most of the SET professions, career advancement to the higher levels, and increased self confidence and job satisfaction, are usually linked with becoming known outside the confines of your particular job.

Becoming more involved in your profession generally (rather than just in your particular job) and in public life should therefore be built into your career planning. It will broaden your experience, help you to develop new skills and expertise, provide you with relevant feedback and heighten your visibility. In addition you will have the satisfaction of knowing that your unique SET expertise is benefitting the wider community.

Speaking up

It is particularly important that *women* in SET achieve a higher profile in order to provide positive role models and encourage more girls and women to think about science and engineering careers. But where do you start?

- Have you thought about volunteering to speak in schools or to talk to groups about science and technology? That's how Sue Bird, profiled on page 200, began her involvement in public life. Why not register your name with an appropriate database of speakers such as Talking Science+ at the British Association for the Advancement of Science? Become a Neighbourhood Engineer or work with WISE at the Engineering Council? Or support the initiatives of your nearest SATRO (Science and Technology Regional Organisation) in local schools?

- What about joining a SET-related voluntary body such as an environmental group? This could give you some experience of action-oriented committees.

- Are you available for media interviews, both locally and nationally? Your local radio might be relieved to find it has an 'expert' at the end of the phone and this would be a good place for you to develop your broadcasting skills. Nationally, several databases are maintained for the purpose of putting journalists and media researchers in touch with SET experts, including the Media Resource Service (MRS) run by the Ciba Foundation and Media Representatives at the Institute of Physics.

- What about contacting your professional association or society to find out what it offers the general public in terms of information and events, and investigating how you can help?

- Why not consider serving on a committee of your professional organisation, whether that is the Institution of Civil Engineers or the Women Chemists Committee of the Royal Society of Chemistry or the London Mathematical Society?

- Have you tried writing articles for the non-technical journals in your field, or for 'popular' science publications such as *New Scientist* or national newspapers? (The books listed on page 202 might help you to 'translate' your science for the general public.)

- If you are a member of a university, what about taking on some extra responsibilities which may be significant outside the university?

- Do you accept invitations to speak not just at conferences in your own field, but also in related fields – for example, if you are a mathematician, the research areas of biology where mathematics has played, or could play, an important role?

- If you would like to get your name on selective databases, you can consult the Women in Science, Technology and Engineering Catalogue of Databases at the Government's Development Unit for Women in SET at the OST (Office of Science and Technology) to find out which ones are available.

Finding out more

- COPUS (the Committee on the Public Understanding of Science) is supported by a number of scientific organisations and aims to bring the whole range of sciences from astronomy to zoology into greater public focus. It organises a variety of initiatives and also runs a COPUS Media Fellowship Scheme.

- *Going Public* (details on page 202) offers useful tips on giving talks, writing readable articles and generally communicating with the public effectively.

- The addresses of the organisations mentioned in the above sections can be found on pages 207-212.

Stepping out

As you build up your experience and expertise, you may wish to broaden the scope of your activities, and put yourself forward for service on a public body, particularly one which is related to your career or interests.

Almost every aspect of our lives is touched by public bodies: the many thousands of organisations which serve the public and help to ensure the relatively smooth running of our society. Some are huge – such as the National Health Service – while others are small – for instance, the governing committee of the local infant school. All are important – and it is equally important that the people who take up public appointments and serve on public bodies truly represent the range of interests in our society.

Many public appointments are very much part-time, often meeting only a few times a year, and many are unpaid (although you may be reimbursed for travel costs, childcare and other expenses). They do not usually involve extensive training, but you will undoubtedly develop new skills as you carry out your duties.

Public appointments can be roughly divided into local, regional and national appointments. There are 'subdivisions' within these categories, such as nationalised industries, consumer watchdogs, advisory bodies and so on. (International appointments are also possible.) The following table gives you an indication of the range of appointments available and a very brief summary of what they might involve.

You might start by getting involved in a non-SET local public body, and as you gain confidence and expertise, work towards an appointment on a national public body relevant to SET.

	Types of appointments include	What might an appointment involve?	Desirable skills and qualifications
Local	school governors magistrates or justices of the peace local health councils National Health Service trusts social security appeal tribunals income tax commissioners prison boards of visitors and visiting committees (in Scotland) valuation tribunals	community-level involvement immediate local issues practical decision-making	live or work in the community concerned no specific qualifications or experience commitment to improve the quality of life for people in your locality

Cont'd over page

	Types of appointments include	What might an appointment involve?	Desirable skills and qualifications
Regional	sports councils regional arts boards health authorities water industry customer service committees tourist boards the Police Authority for Northern Ireland TECs (England) LECs (Scotland) Business Links	implementing government policies in your region	knowledge of and/or involvement in the region specialist experience (e.g. SET) professional knowledge and expertise
National	everything from the BBC to racial equality or breast cancer screening, for example: Commission for Racial Equality Royal Commission on Environmental Pollution Gas Consumers' Council Radioactive Waste Management Advisory Commission National Advisory Council on Employment of People with Disabilities National Museum of Science & Industry National Food Survey Committee National Rivers Authority Royal Botanic Garden (Edinburgh) Offshore Energy Technology Board Equal Opportunities Commission and hundreds more	almost anything and everything!	a mix of specialists, professionals and lay people – so you're bound to fit in somewhere!

Your country needs you!

Over half the population is female. Over half the nation's 'resources' are female. Over half the talent is female. Over half the experience is female.

So why aren't at least half the members of our public bodies female?

The Government itself is keen to increase the number of public appointments held by women and has published departmental goals which range from 25% to 50%. Unfortunately the simple fact remains: to be chosen for a public appointment, it has to be known that you are available and willing as well as suitable, and many women hesitate to put themselves forward for one reason or another.

This problem is exacerbated with SET-related committees and boards, as the Government and other bodies often find it difficult to identify women with the appropriate SET experience in the first place. Progress has been made in this respect with the establishment of specific databases of SET women experts (see page 190), and now might be the time for *you* to consider putting *your* name forward.

Why should *you* do it?

Women who have served on various public bodies usually find they gain a great deal from the experience.

- 'It's confidence-building. I find my judgement matters even though it's common sense really.' Environmental officer
- 'It's a challenge!' Systems analyst
- 'Being self-employed as a computer consultant, I've found public service is a useful way to increase my visibility.' Computer consultant
- 'It's fun. You meet lots of new and fascinating people, all of whom are subsequently people you can network with, and who are useful contacts.' Mechanical engineer
- 'You can feel that you are contributing to the efficient running of the country.' Research biologist
- 'It's been interesting. And I've acquired a different range of skills and experiences to those I've developed as a lecturer in microbiology.' Microbiologst
- 'I saw it as an opportunity to change something I thought should be changed.' Civil engineer
- 'It might sound wet, but I just wanted to give something back to the community.' Government scientist
- 'I enjoy it.' Laboratory technician

- 'It's a marvellous way of gaining access to different networks. I've met people from a broad spectrum of backgrounds whom I would not otherwise meet.' Acoustics engineer

- 'I'm power-hungry! I like influencing the course of events.' Production manager

- I'd been at home with the children for six years and lost confidence. Becoming a school governor has helped me to believe that I have something to offer, especially when I helped to implement a new science curriculum.' Biologist

- 'I like the feeling that I'm part of the national decision-making process.' Materials scientist

- 'I would rate serving on *The Rising Tide* working group as one of my greatest achievements. It really changed things.' Academic scientist

Dr Lynn Gladden's experience highlights some of the benefits of taking up a public appointment.

Dr Lynn Gladden, chemical engineer

Dr Lynn Gladden is in her mid 30s. She has a first degree in chemical physics from the University of Bristol and did a PhD in the structure of amorphous materials in the Department of Physical Chemistry at the University of Cambridge. She now works in the Department of Chemical Engineering at Cambridge, but also spends typically one month a year working in industry.

My PhD work led to my first public appointment as a member of the Neutron Beam Research Committee which aimed to develop an overall strategy for neutron research in the UK, linked into global developments. The committee had members from both industry and academia, but I was one of the few women on it.

My work on that committee led me to others, and most recently I've been on the Government's Technology Foresight Panel. The original remit was a 20-year forward look at the important areas of SET. That was an immense brief, and what we ended up doing was a 'state-of-the-art' assessment of current strengths and weaknesses, with recommendations as to which areas might be considered as priority areas. The Technology Foresight Panel has now moved into its second phase which is to identify areas of industrial and economic relevance. We want to ensure that ideas are put into practice, and that feedback from industry will ensure that what's happening in the universities – both in terms of teaching and research – can be used not only by the large companies but also in the smaller ones.

Committees can be very time-consuming and on occasions I wonder how much more research I would have done if I wasn't on them. However, until recently I was the only chemical engineer in my department working in the field of catalysis and magnetic resonance and even though I spend time working in industry every year, my relative 'isolation' meant it would be very easy for me to produce work that wasn't relevant.

Liaising with committee members from industry keeps me on track. Not only can I test out my initial ideas, but while I'm working on a particular line of research I can get feedback which might help me to 'tweak' a project by 5% and thereby make it 100% more effective. My links with industry also help me to get my work tested and implemented.

My public appointments have definitely influenced the direction and focus of my career.

For most appointments – whether at the local, regional or national level – you will need many of the skills you will have built up through your career in SET. These might include the ability to:

- both speak out and listen in a group situation
- deal with large amounts of information
- work out what the issues are
- analyse the essential arguments
- consider the pros and cons of a particular situation objectively
- evaluate the implications of a course of action impartially
- demonstrate common sense and fairness
- make and take tough decisions.

Most importantly, you need to have a genuine interest in the issues you will be dealing with.

If you don't feel quite ready for a public appointment at this stage in your life, you might like to get involved in voluntary work or local politics, as the experience and the contacts you make will prove very valuable if you want to be considered for a public appointment in the future.

When should you do it?

Inevitably the problem most women will have when it comes to considering a public appointment is one of time: how do you fit everything in? If you have family commitments, adding 'public service' to the roles you already have may seem to be an extra burden.

However you could think about a public appointment:

- before you have children – younger people are often under-represented and welcome on many bodies
- during a career break – it can be a means of staying in circulation, acquiring new skills and experience, and keeping up your confidence levels
- when your children are older – a public appointment can be a way of broadening your horizons and moving into a different sphere.

And remember, for many public appointments, you may be reimbursed for childcare expenses.

So you could think about putting your name forward right now ...

How do *you* apply?

For regional and national appointments, you could contact the Public Appointments Unit (see below). The Public Appointments Unit in London holds a list of names of people interested in having a public appointment, and this is used by ministers and others responsible for making such appointments. The Scottish Office, the Welsh Office and the Northern Ireland Office each maintain similar public appointments registers.

Don't say no!

You might argue that you do not have the relevant experience that would make you a useful member of a public body.

Quite apart from the valuable expertise you can contribute as a woman in SET, the skills and experience acquired from your interests outside your career – from any voluntary work you have done, or from your position as a member of a family unit – make you a viable member of a public body.

The Public Appointments Unit

You can nominate yourself for the register, or get someone to nominate you. Although being on the register will not guarantee you a position, it is a start. Find out more from:

The Public Appointments Unit
Cabinet Office
Horse Guards Road
London SW1P 3AL

The Central Appointments Unit
Central Secretariat
Stormont Castle
Belfast
BT4 3ST

The Public Appointments Unit
The Scottish Office
Management Support Group
St Andrew's House
Edinburgh
EH1 3DE

The Public Appointments Branch
Management Planning and Review
Division
Welsh Office
Cathays Park
Cardiff
CF1 3NQ

Alternatively, you could apply to be added to the Database of Expert Women in SET which is maintained by WITEC (Women in Technology). This database covers much of Europe and offers you the possibility of serving on European committees as well as those in the UK.

WITEC (Women in Technology)

WITEC is 'a European network of universities, companies and individuals working to support and encourage women studying and working in science, engineering and technology'. WITEC was established in 1988 and is supported by the Commission of the European Communities. WITEC UK is based at Sheffield Hallam University, along with the Secretariat which coordinates the European network.

WITEC's activities include national and international networking, information on European SET programmes, short training courses, lobbying work for the EU's research and training programmes, student placements, information and equal opportunities advice. As well as all these activities, membership of WITEC 'will give you access to a wealth of expertise relating to equal opportunities and will create opportunities for networking and involvement in European project work'.

As part of its initiative to raise the profile of eminent women across Europe (with the main aim of increasing the number of women on expert committees and advisory groups), WITEC has produced the *European Handbook of Women Experts in Science, Engineering and Technology* (published 1996). The handbook contains 'summary CVs of 1350 women experts from 14 member states' who wish to be considered for appointment to public bodies in Europe.

WITEC is keeping the handbook up-to-date on computer, so new names continue to be added as more women become aware of the project. Why not consider applying to WITEC for inclusion in the database?

For more information contact:

WITEC (Women in Technology)
Sheffield Hallam University
Heriot House
City Campus
Sheffield
S1 1WB
Tel: 0114 253 2041; fax: 0114 253 2046; email: Witec@shu.ac.uk

Another option, particularly for regional or general appointments, is to apply through the Women's National Commission (see page 198). The WNC is frequently asked to suggest suitable names for consideration for various positions, and its publications include a general application form which you can complete and submit for inclusion in the WNC list of candidates. Note that one of the questions on this form allows you to demonstrate what you have learned from your activities outside the workplace. It says: 'Please write below a brief "self appraisal" of what you feel you would bring to a public appointment by way of experience, interests, skills, etc. You are welcome to include details any special circumstances such as bringing up children, experience with a disabled child or caring for an elderly or disabled person. Any information which you feel is relevant should be included.'

If you are on a career break, you might find the suggestions on page 128 useful when responding to this question.

The Women's National Commission (WNC)

The WNC is an independent advisory committee to the Government of the day with the remit to 'ensure by all possible means that the informed opinion of women is given its due weight in the deliberations of government'. It has over 80 full and associate member organisations including many trades unions, professional women's organisations, the major political parties and voluntary bodies.

The WNC 'firmly believes that women from all walks of life should be able to make their influence felt in the development and implementation of policies and practices', and works towards achieving a higher proportion of women in public appointments. With this aim in mind it publishes *Stepping Out in Public* and *Public Appointments. A directory for women.*

Stepping Out in Public describes the types of public appointment in more detail, and also includes profiles of women who have taken those 'first steps'. It guides you through the process of applying for a public appointment, how to produce an effective application, and how to be successful at interviews. It also provides a general application form, a useful list of addresses and suggestions for further reading.

Public Appointments. A directory for women is a comprehensive handbook which seeks to remedy the lack of information about posts available on public bodies and what is involved if you take up an appointment. The *Directory* enables you to find out:

- which organisations are in your areas of interest and experience
- where they are located
- how much time the specific posts take up
- what background, qualifications and expertise are required
- whether they are paid or unpaid, and other basic facts and practical details
- how many men and how many women are currently on the various bodies

- which departments make the appointments
- where you can find further information.

You can obtain these publications free of charge from the WNC at:

The Women's National Commission
Caxton House
Tothill Street
London SW1H 9NF
Tel: 0171 273 5486; fax: 0171 962 8171

Applying for a public appointment is like applying for a paid job: you need to do your homework on the organisation, define your skills and areas of experience with regard to the position in question, work out what you have to offer them and develop an appropriate application/CV. You might find it helpful to refer back to Chapter 3 for information on job applications and interviews.

The 300 Group

Of course the best-known 'public decision-making body' of all is Parliament, and even after the 1997 election women are still under-represented there! The 300 Group 'crosses' all the political parties with its mission of getting more women into Parliament. Its aims include equipping women with the necessary skills for public life and increasing public awareness. Membership is open to both women and men, and there are branches throughout the UK. If you are interested, contact:

The 300 Group
PO Box 353
Uxbridge
UB10 OUN
Tel/fax: 01895 812 229

Anne Campbell, the current MP for Cambridge, is profiled on page 161. She has a degree in mathematics, lectured in statistics, and has been a member of various Parliamentary science and technology committees.

Sue Bird, consultant engineer in acoustics and noise control

Sue Bird took a BSc in Applied Physics at Coventry University. She worked for the British Aircraft Corporation (BAC) for three years and the Greater London Council (GLC) scientific branch for 12 years, before deciding to become self-employed in 1986. She is in her late 40s. In this profile she explains why and how she 'stepped into' public life.

It's magic working with aircraft and I enjoyed my time at BAC working as an acoustic engineer; I also relished the variety of work at the GLC where I never knew what was going to come up: pop concerts one day, railways the next and testifying as an expert witness in a nuisance case the day after that. Working for the ratepayer gave me a great sense of satisfaction. Now I get that same sense of satisfaction from some of the public appointments I hold, as I feel I am giving back something to my profession.

It started through my membership of the Women's Engineering Society (WES). I like working with men but I originally joined WES because I appreciated being able to meet other women in the same line of work as myself. For many years my involvement with WES was low-key, although I did visit schools and colleges to give talks on careers in engineering. I felt it was important to convey to girls that engineering was an option that could offer them a great deal, and one that they should at least consider.

I became Junior Vice President of WES in 1987. By then I had started my own consultancy in acoustics and noise control, working for clients such as architects, builders and local authorities – in fact anybody who needed advice on minimising the impact of noise, whether that noise was from a road, a factory fan or an inadequately insulated hall. I found that WES was a good way of keeping in touch with changes in the engineering field and of networking – as well as a means of making friends and enhancing my social life!

My first four years in self-employment were very busy but then I suffered from the classic problem of having most of my eggs in one basket – my client base was mainly the building trade and consequently I was affected by the slump in the construction industry in the early 1990s. It was then that I was elected as President of WES.

The position was unpaid but in other respects it was very rewarding. When you are self-employed and things are slow, it is all too easy to get depressed: being WES President meant I actually had something to do, and I could continue to contribute to society in a useful way.
The presidency allowed me to build up skills I didn't have before: I learned to chair meetings, to make presentations, and developed fundraising abilities. Previously I'd found it awkward asking people to settle overdue invoices, but during my presidency I became quite used to making 'cold calls' and asking for money! I also met people I wouldn't have otherwise come into contact with – the captains of industry and other decision-makers.

My WES experience had even more tangible benefits. The Institute of Acoustics has only been able to award Chartered Engineering status relatively recently. When I applied, I had to provide evidence of management experience. This could have been a problem as I do not have anyone working directly for me. Fortunately I was able to cite my years of managing volunteers as WES President.

As a result of my 'exposure' at WES I was asked to serve on the Office of Science and Technology Working Group in SET (which resulted in the publication of *The Rising Tide*) and after that I decided to put my name forward to the Public Appointments Unit (see page 196). I was quite surprised when my name was selected from the list and I was invited to sit on the LINK Board, which is responsible for distributing £30 million of government money to joint industrial and academic research projects. I looked at the criteria for membership: it seemed to be all vice-chancellors and directors of large companies. 'Was I really the person they wanted?' I queried. 'Yes,' they said. I now sit on the LINK Board and try to represent the SMEs (the small- and medium-sized enterprises).

Currently I hold several public appointments. One I find fascinating is my governorship of Welbeck College, a sixth-form college for future army officers in the Engineering Corps. When the college had its first intake of female students, I was invited to become a governor by someone who knew of my work as WES President and who thought it would be a good idea to have a female engineer on the board.

To any woman who is contemplating a public appointment, I'd say go ahead. It will be hard work but the more you put in, the more you'll get out of it. You don't have to be brilliant: you just have to say what you know, suggest what you can do – and do it. It really is as simple as that.

Working for myself perhaps makes it easier for me to get involved in different things, but with a fast-expanding business, I still have to make choices about where and how I manage my time and energy. However, I look on my public appointments as a means of broadening my field of operations and serving my profession – and it certainly makes my life more interesting. Just after I had finished my term of office as WES President I had the opportunity to go to New Zealand to lecture on CPD (Continuing Professional Development). I didn't know anything about CPD then, but with a three-week all-expenses paid trip in prospect, I made sure I found out and now chair the Institute of Acoustics CPD Committee!

Speaking up

Going Public: an introduction to communicating science, engineering and technology

Published and obtainable from the Department of Trade and Industry or on website: http://www.open.gov.uk/osthome.htm

A brief booklet on the hows and whys of getting involved with the public – and the ways in which you can ensure you do so effectively!

Communicating Science: a handbook

Michael Shortland and Jane Gregory, Longman Scientific & Technical, 1991

This handbook covers in depth the different ways of communicating science to the public.

RSA Directory of Women Speakers

Compiled and published by the Royal Society of Arts (RSA). Regularly updated

This directory is published regularly by the RSA in response to the demand for more female speakers on a variety of issues. (The address of the RSA is given on page 211.) The *Directory* is divided into a number of categories such as engineering, consumer affairs and science. Speakers can make themselves available for a variety of engagements including media interviews, written articles, plenary conferences, seminar talks, panel discussions and school events. Variable fees are charged, but the majority of speakers agree to speak to charities either free of charge or for expenses only. What about you?

Stepping out

Time Off for Public Duties

This DTI leaflet – PL 702 (Rev 1) – gives general guidance on the provisions relating to time off for public duties. Note that while employers are required to permit employees who hold certain public positions reasonable time off to perform the duties associated with them, they are under no obligation to pay you for that time.

You can obtain this leaflet free from your local jobcentre or library or telephone 0171 273 6969.

Public Bodies

Cabinet Office, Office of Public Service, HMSO, updated annually

This lists the nationalised industries and non-departmental public bodies currently in existence and is intended as a first point of reference on these bodies. It also includes information on the number and gender of individuals appointed.

And don't forget *Stepping Out in Public* and *Public Appointments. A directory for women*, published by the WNC (see page 198-99).

Author's acknowledgements

A book such as this one is a massive undertaking and so many people have helped in so many ways over the long months of its creation: where do I begin?

Perhaps at the beginning – I would like to thank Rosemary Scott for alerting me to the email that started the whole process of my involvement, and the generous sponsors of the book who made its publication possible.

I may have been the author, but this book would not have existed without the powerful impetus of the members of its Executive Committee. In particular I personally would like to convey my gratitude to Nancy Lane, who chaired the meetings with such expertise and enabled us to get through a great deal of decision-making in a remarkably short time; Ann Bailey, particularly for her invaluable advice on action plans and transferable skills; Marie-Noëlle Barton, who shouldered the heavy administrative responsibility and the all-important and difficult task of finding a publisher; Joan Mason, who hospitably allowed me access to her amazingly comprehensive sources of information; Libby Steele, who kept the book focused and provided the necessary information to enable me to do so; and to Judith Howard, Mary Phillips, Caroline Roberts, Lynda Sharp and Janet Whitaker who have all contributed to improving the book and helped in its publication.

A special thanks must go to Judith May, who had the original idea for this book and advised at every stage with skill and precision.

Lily Segerman-Peck kindly reviewed Chapter 4, saved me from making a fatal omission, and made many valuable suggestions, all of which I incorporated. The Daphne Jackson Memorial Fellowships Trust offered helpful advice and information on Chapter 7, and members of the Executive Committee reviewed the other chapters. For any errors and omissions, however, I alone am responsible.

Next I would like to express my gratitude to the profilees named within the text, and to Anthony Cohen, Cornelia McLean, Patricia Steen, and all the many others whose brains I picked and whose insights I used; to the people and organisations who kindly supplied me with information, names, addresses and further leads; to Hayley Whitebread at the Engineering Council who dealt with the repeated avalanches of paper with great cheerfulness and speed; and to Siân Jones and her colleagues at Training Publications Limited who worked hard to meet the challenging deadlines.

The author and publisher would also like to thank the authors and publishers whose works are quoted in this book, including the National Childbirth Trust and NCT Publishing for permission to reproduce a shortened version of an article on maternity rights that first appeared in its magazine, *Pregnancy Plus*, and The Royal Society and The British Association for the Advancement of Science as the publishers of *Science and Public Affairs*, for the amended extracts of the article by Claire Goodess on short-term contracts. The short extracts from *The Rising Tide* on pages

94, 121, 133, 146, 155 and 187 and from *Women and Employment* on page 121, are copyright and are reproduced with the permission of the Controller of Her Majesty's Stationery Office. The short extracts from *HL Paper 60 The Dainton Report* on pages 143 and 145 are Parliamentary copyright and are reproduced with the permission of the Controller of Her Majesty's Stationery Office. The IEEIE kindly provided two of the cover photographs.

Finally, I would like to thank Amy and Julian who put up with my 'distraction' and too many frozen chips throughout the writing of *Cracking it!*, and who make me practise what I preach about balancing work and home.

Acronyms

ABPI Association of the British Pharmaceutical Industry

AGR Association of Graduate Recruiters

AMBA Association of MBAs

AMRC Association of Medical Research Charities

APL Accreditation of Prior Learning

AUT Association of University Teachers

AWiSE Association for Women in Science and Engineering

BBSRC Biotechnology and Biological Sciences Research Council

CASI Compact Airborne Spectrographic Imager

CATS Credit Accumulation and Transfer Scheme

CCLRC Council for the Central Laboratory of the Research Councils

CDL Career Development Loan

COIC Careers and Occupational Information Centre

COPUS Committee on the Public Understanding of Science

CPD Continuing Professional Development

CV Curriculum Vitae

CVCP Committee of Vice-Chancellors and Principals

DfEE Department for Education and Employment

DTI Department of Trade and Industry

ECCTIS Education Counselling and Credit Transfer Information Service

EEF Engineering Employers' Federation

EMTA Engineering and Marine Training Authority

EOC Equal Opportunities Commission

EPSRC Engineering and Physical Sciences Research Council

GCHQ Government Communications Headquarters

GNVQ General National Vocational Qualification

HMSO Her Majesty's Stationery Office

HNC Higher National Certificate

HND Higher National Diploma

ICDL International Centre for Distance Learning

LEC Local Enterprise Company

MA Maternity Allowance

MBA Master of Business Administration

MRC Medical Research Council

MRS Media Resource Service

NCT National Childbirth Trust

NERC Natural Environment Research Council

NOW New Opportunities for Women

NVQ National Vocational Qualification

ONC Ordinary National Certificate

OND Ordinary National Diploma

OST Office of Science and Technology

OU Open University

PPARC Particle Physics and Astronomy Research Council

PTA Parent Teacher Association

QCA Qualifications Curriculum Authority

QP Qualified Person

QTS Qualified Teacher Status

RSA Royal Society of Arts

SATRO Science and Technology Regional Organisation

SET Science, Engineering and Technology

SMEs Small- and Medium-sized Enterprises

SMP Statutory Maternity Pay

SRIS (The British Library) Science Reference and Information Service

SWOT Strengths, Weaknesses, Opportunities and Threats

T&EA Training and Employment Agency

TAP Training Access Point

TEC Training and Enterprise Council

UCAS Universities and Colleges Admissions Service

WES Women's Engineering Society

WISE Women Into Science and Engineering

WITEC Women in Technology

WNC Women's National Commission

Useful addresses

The following list of addresses is indicative, rather than inclusive, and includes many of the professional and learned societies, women's networking organisations and other significant 'SET' addresses.

African-Caribbean Network for Science & Technology
Ishango House
447 Chester Road
Old Trafford
Manchester
M16 9HA
Tel: 0161 877 1480; fax: 0161 877 1481

The Association for Science Education
College Lane
Hatfield
Herts
AL10 9AA
Tel: 01707 267 411; fax: 01707 266 532;
website: http://www.rmplc.co.uk/orgs/asehq/index.html; email: ase@asehq.tellme.com

Association for Women in Science and Engineering (AWiSE)
AWiSE National Office
1 Park Square West
London
NW1 4LJ
Tel: 0171 935 3282/5202; fax: 0171 935 0736;
email: awise@wellcome.ac.uk
website: http://www.awise.org

Association of Medical Research Charities (AMRC)
29–35 Farringdon Road
London
EC1M 3JB
Tel: 0171 404 6454; fax: 0171 404 6448
email: amrc@mailbox.ulcc.ac.uk

The Association of the British Pharmaceutical Industry (ABPI)
12 Whitehall
London SW1A 2DY
Tel: 0171 930 3477; fax: 0171 747 1411;
website: http://www.abpi.org.uk
email: ia@abpi.co.uk

The Association of University Teachers (AUT)
United House
9 Pembridge Road
London
W11 3JY
Tel: 0171 221 4370; fax: 0171 727 6547;
website: http://www.aut.org.uk; AUT (Scotland) website:
http://www.aut.org.uk.scotaut/auts/html
email: hq@aut.org.uk

Biochemical Society
59 Portland Place
London
W1N 3AJ
Tel: 0171 580 5530; fax: 0171 637 7626

Biotechnology and Biological Sciences Research Council (BBSRC)
Polaris House
North Star Avenue
Swindon
SN2 1UH
Tel: 01793 413 200; fax: 01793 413 201;
website: http://www.bbsrc.ac.uk

British Association for the Advancement of Science (BAAS)
23 Savile Row
London
W1X 2NB
Tel: 0171 973 3500; fax: 0171 973 3051;
website: http://www.britassoc.org.uk

The British Computer Society
1 Sanford Street
Swindon
SN1 1HJ
Tel: 01793 417 417; fax: 01793 480 270;
website: http://www.bcs.org.uk
email: bcshq@bcs.org.uk

British Pharmacological Society
16 Angel Gate
City Road
London EC1V 2PT
Tel: 0171 417 0113; fax: 0171 417 0114

Business and Professional Women UK Ltd
23 Ansdell Street
London
W8 5BN
Tel: 0171 938 1729; fax: 0171 938 2037

**Careers and Occupational Information
Centre (COIC)**
Moorfoot
Sheffield
S1 4PQ
Tel: 0114 275 3275

**Chartered Institution of Building Services
Engineers**
Delta House
222 Balham High Road
London
SW12 9BS
Tel: 0181 675 5211; fax: 0181 675 5449;
website: http: //www.cibse.org

**Chartered Institution of Water and
Environmental Management**
15 John Street
London
WC1N 2EB
Tel: 0171 831 3110; fax: 0171 405 4967;
website: http://www.ciwem.co.uk

The Ciba Foundation
41 Portland Place
London
W1N 4BN
Tel: 0171 636 9456; fax: 0171 436 2840;
website: http://www.ciba.foundation.demon.
org.uk

**Commission for Racial Equality
Headquarters Office**
Elliot House
10–12 Allington Street
London
SW1E 5EH
Tel: 0171 828 7022; fax: 0171 630 7605

**Committee on the Public Understanding of
Science (COPUS)**
c/o The Royal Society
6 Carlton House Terrace
London
SW1Y 5AG
Tel: 0171 451 2580; fax: 0171 451 2693

**Council for the Central Laboratory of the
Research Councils (CCLRC)**
Rutherford Appleton Laboratory
Chilton
Didcot
Oxfordshire
OX11 1QX
Tel: 01235 445 475; fax: 01235 445 584;
website http://www.cclrc.ac.uk

**The Daphne Jackson Memorial
Fellowships Trust**
Department of Physics
University of Surrey
Guildford
Surrey
GU2 5XH
Tel: 01483 259 166; fax: 01483 259 501;
website: http://www.sst.ph.ic.ac.uk/trust/

**Development Unit for Women in SET
Office of Science and Technology (OST)**
UG.A.36/B35
1 Victoria Street
London
SW1H 0ET
Tel: 0171 215 0047; fax: 0171 215 0054

EEF (Engineering Employers' Federation)
Broadway House
Tothill Street
London
SW1H 9NQ
Tel: 0171 222 7777; fax: 0171 222 2782;
website: http://www.eef.org.uk; email: eef-
fed.org.uk

**Engineering and Marine Training
Authority (EMTA)**
Vector House
41 Clarendon Road
Watford
Hertfordshire
WD1 1HS
Tel: 01923 238 441; fax: 01923 256 086

**Engineering and Physical Sciences
Research Council (EPSRC)**
Polaris House
North Star Avenue
Swindon
SN2 1ET
Tel: 01793 444 000; fax: 01793 444 010;
website: http://www.epsrc.ac.uk

Engineering Council
10 Maltravers Street
London
WC2R 3ER
Tel: 0171 240 7891; fax: 0171 240 7517

Equal Opportunities Commission
Overseas House
Quay Street
Manchester
M3 3HN
Tel: 0161 833 9244; fax: 0161 835 1657

Equal Opportunities Commission for Northern Ireland
Chamber of Commerce House
22 Great Victoria Street
Belfast
BT2 7BA

European Women's Management Development Network (EWMD)
Rue Washington 40
B-1050 Brussels
Belgium
Tel: 00 32 2 648 03 85; fax: 00 32 2 646 07 68

The Fawcett Society
Fifth Floor
45 Beech Street
London
EC2Y 8AD
Tel: 0171 628 4441; fax: 0171 628 2865

Geological Society
Burlington House
Piccadilly
London
W1V 0JU
Tel: 0171 434 9944

Geologists' Association
Burlington House
Piccadilly
London
W1V 9AG
Tel: 0171 434 9298; fax: 0171 287 0280;
email: geol.assoc@btinternet.com

Institute of Biology
20–22 Queensberry Place
London
SW7 2DZ
Tel: 0171 581 8333; fax: 0171 823 9409;
website: http://www.primex.co.uk/iob

Institute of Energy
18 Devonshire Street
London
W1N 2AU
Tel: 0171 580 7124; fax: 0171 580 4420;
website: http://www.instenergy.org.uk

Institute of Highway Incorporated Engineers
20 Queensberry Place
London
SW7 2DR
Tel: 0171 823 9093; fax: 0171 581 8087;
email: ihie@dial.pipex.com

The Institute of Marine Engineers
The Memorial Building
76 Mark Lane
London
EC3R 7JN
Tel: 0171 481 8493; fax: 0171 488 1854;
email: imare@imare.org.uk

Institute of Materials
1 Carlton House Terrace
London
SW1Y 5DB
Tel: 0171 839 4071; fax: 0171 839 1702

Institute of Physics
(Women in Physics Group)
76 Portland Place
London
W1N 4AA
Tel: 0171 470 4800; fax: 0171 470 4848;
website: http://www.iop.org

Institution of Chemical Engineers
Davis Building
165–189 Railway Terrace
Rugby
Warwickshire
CV21 3HQ
Tel: 01788 578 214; fax: 01788 560 833

Institution of Civil Engineers
1–7 Great George Street
London
SW1P 3AA
Tel: 0171 222 7722; fax: 0171 222 7500

Institution of Electrical Engineers
Savoy Place
London
WC2R 0BL
Tel: 0171 240 1871; fax: 0171 240 7735;
website: http://www.iee.org.uk

Institution of Electronics and Electrical Incorporated Engineers
Savoy Hill House
Savoy Hill
London
WC2R 0BS
Tel: 0171 836 3357; fax: 0171 497 9006

Institution of Mechanical Engineers
Northgate Avenue
Bury St Edmunds
Suffolk
IP32 6BN
Tel: 01284 763 277; fax: 01284 704 006;
website: http://www.imeche.org.uk

also at
1 Birdcage Walk
London
SW1H 9JJ
Tel: 0171 222 7899; fax: 0171 222 4557

Institution of Mechanical Incorporated Engineers
3 Birdcage Walk
Westminster
London
SW1H 9JN
Tel: 0171 799 1808; fax; 0171 799 2243

Institution of Mining and Metallurgy
44 Portland Place
London
W1N 4BR
Tel: 0171 580 3802; fax: 0171 436 5388;
website: http://www.imm.org.uk

Institution of Mining Engineers
Danum House
South Parade
Doncaster
DN1 2DY
Tel: 01302 320 486; fax: 01302 340 554;
email: imine@clara.net

Institution of Nuclear Engineers
1 Penerley Road
London
SE6 2LQ
Tel: 0181 698 1500; fax: 0181 695 6409

Institution of Structural Engineers
11 Upper Belgrave Street
London
SW1X 8BH
Tel: 0171 235 4535; fax: 0171 235 4294

Investors in People UK
4th Floor
7–10 Chandos Street
London
W1M 9DE
Tel: 0171 467 1900; fax: 0171 636 2386;
website: http://www.investors/in/people/
uk@dial.pipex.com

The Linnean Society
Burlington House
Piccadilly
London
W1V 0LQ
Tel: 0171 434 4479; fax: 0171 287 9364;
website: http://www.linnean.org.uk

London Mathematical Society
Burlington House
Piccadilly
London
W1V 0NL
Tel: 0171 437 5377; fax: 0171 439 4629;
website: http://www.lms.ac.uk

Medical Research Council (MRC)
20 Park Crescent
London
W1N 4AL
Tel: 0171 636 5422; fax: 0171 636 6179;
website: http://www.mrc.ac.uk

Natural Environment Research Council (NERC)
Polaris House
North Star Avenue
Swindon
SN1 1DE
Tel: 01793 411 500; fax: 01793 411 501;
website: http://www.nerc.ac.uk

Network for Successful UK Women
114B Cleveland Street
London
W1P 5DN
Tel: 0171 388 7383; fax: 0181 961 7468

Office of Science and Technology (OST)
Albany House
94-98 Petty France
London
SW1H 9ST
Tel: 0171 271 2000

Opportunity 2000
Business in the Community
44 Baker Street
London
W1M 1DH
Tel: 0171 224 1600; fax: 0171 486 1700;
website: http://info.lut.ac.uk/orgs/opp2000/

Particle Physics and Astronomy Research Council (PPARC)
Polaris House
North Star Avenue
Swindon
SN2 1SZ
Tel: 01793 442 000; fax: 01793 442 106;
website: http://www.pparc.ac.uk

Royal Academy of Engineering
29 Great Peter Street
London
SW1P 3LW
Tel: 0171 222 2688; fax: 0171 233 0054

Royal Aeronautical Society
4 Hamilton Place
London
W1V 0BQ
Tel: 0171 499 3515; fax: 0171 499 6230;
website: http://www.raes/raes.org.uk
email: raes@raes.org.uk

Royal Astronomical Society
Burlington House
Piccadilly
London
W1V 0NL
Tel: 0171 734 4582; fax: 0171 494 0166;
email: info@ras.org.uk

The Royal Institution of Great Britain (RI)
21 Albemarle Street
London
W1X 4BS
Tel: 0171 409 2992; fax: 0171 629 3569

Royal Pharmaceutical Society of Great Britain
1 Lambeth High Street
London
SE1 7JN
Tel: 0171 735 9141; fax: 0171 735 7629

The Royal Society
6 Carlton House Terrace
London
SW1Y 5AG
Tel: 0171 839 5561; fax: 0171 930 2170;
website: http://www. roalsoc.ac.uk
email: ezmb013@mailbox.ulcc.ac.uk

Royal Society of Arts (RSA)
8 John Adam Street
London
WC2N 6EZ
Tel: 0171 930 5115; fax: 0171 839 5805;
email: rsa@rsa.ftech.co.uk

Royal Society of Chemistry (Women Chemists' Committee)
Burlington House
Piccadilly
London
W1V 0BN
Tel: 0171 437 8656; fax: 0171 437 8883;
website: http://www.chemistry.rsc.org/rsc/

Royal Society of Edinburgh
22–24 George Street
Edinburgh
EH2 2PQ
Tel: 0131 225 6057; fax: 0131 220 6889;
website: http://www.ma.hw.ac.uk/rse/
email: rse@rse.org.uk

**SATROs (Science and Technology Regional Organisations)
contactable through:
Standing Conference on Schools' Science and Technology (SCSST)**
1 Giltspur Street
London
EC1A 9DD
Tel: 0171 294 2431; fax: 0171 294 2442

Skill – The National Bureau for Students with Disabilities
336 Brixton Road
London
SW9 7AA
Tel: 0171 274 0565; fax: 0171 737 7477;
email: skillnatburdis@compuserve.com or
101356.3005@compuserve.com
information line: 0171 978 9890;
minicom: 0171 738 7722

Society for General Microbiology
Marlborough House
Basingstoke Road
Spencers Wood
Reading
RG7 1AE
Tel: 0118 988 5577; fax: 0118 988 5656;
email: admin@socgenmicrobiol.org.uk

Trades Union Congress (TUC)
Congress House
Great Russell Street
London
WC1B 3LS
Tel: 0171 636 4030; fax: 0171 636 0632

The Wellcome Trust
183 Euston Road
London
NW1 2BE
Tel: 0171 611 8888; fax: 0171 611 8545;
website: http://www.wellcome.ac.uk

Winning Women Project
Maureen Cooper
Department of Chemistry
University of Stirling
Stirling
FK9 4LA
Tel: 01786 467 781; website: http://
www.dundee.ac.uk/design/winning.html
email: m.e.cooper@stir.ac.uk

WISE (Women Into Science and Engineering)
c/o The Engineering Council

WITEC (Women in Technology)
Sheffield Hallam University
Heriot House
City Campus
Sheffield
S1 1WB
Tel: 0114 253 2041; fax: 0114 253 2046;
email: Witec@shu.ac.uk

Women Chemists' Committee
c/o Royal Society of Chemistry

Women in Higher Education Network
University of Central Lancashire
Preston
PR1 2HE
Tel: 01772 892 391; fax: 01772 892 943

Women in Management
Fifth Floor
45 Beech Street
London
EC2Y 8AD
Tel: 0171 382 9978; fax: 0171 382 9979

Women in Physics Group
c/o Institute of Physics

Women into Computing
c/o Janet Stack
Department of Computing Science
University of Glasgow
7 Lilybank Gardens
Glasgow
G12 8QQ
Tel: 0141 339 8855

Women Returners' Network
100 Park Village East
London
NW1 3SR
Tel: 0171 468 2290; fax: 0171 380 0123

Women's Engineering Society (WES)
Imperial College of Science, Technology and Medicine
Department of Civil Engineering
Imperial College Road
London
SW7 2BU
Tel: 0171 594 6025; fax: 0171 594 6026;
email: wes@ic.ac.uk

Women's National Commission
Caxton House
Tothill Street
London
SW1H 9NF
Tel: 0171 273 5486; fax: 0171 962 8171

The sponsors

The ABPI and the pharmaceutical industry

The Association of the British Pharmaceutical Industry (ABPI) represents companies in Britain that research, develop, manufacture and market prescription medicines. It also has other members drawn from organisations with an interest in the pharmaceutical industry operating in the UK.

Member companies of the ABPI supply more than 90 per cent of the prescription medicines taken up by the NHS. The industry employs around 75 000 people directly and invests more than £2 billion a year in research and development, nearly a quarter of all industrial R&D in the UK. Five out of the world's top 20 prescription medicines were discovered and developed in UK laboratories. Export figures for the pharmaceutical industry achieved a record £5.4 billion in 1996, resulting in a surplus with our trade partners of £2.3 billion.

Development Unit on Women in Science, Engineering and Technology, Office of Science and Technology, DTI

The Government's Development Unit on Women in Science, Engineering and Technology was established in December 1994 within the Office of Science and Technology. The Unit's role is to act primarily as a facilitator working with others to encourage more women into SET in industry and academia. Its responsibilities include:

- encouraging equal opportunities policies and practices with respect to the needs of women in SET
- disseminating good practice
- ensuring adequate access to careers advice on SET
- maintaining a catalogue of databases on women in SET
- and monitoring progress.

EEF

The EEF (Engineering Employers' Federation) is the representational voice of Engineering. It is a federation of 13 Regional Associations and a National Association for engineering construction which embraces over 5300 member companies of all sizes, from various sectors of manufacturing industry (and some sectors of commerce).

On behalf of its members the EEF seeks to influence the decisions of the UK Government and the European institutions to create a favourable business environment for engineering and technology-based manufacturing.

EEF's aims include:

- promoting the image of engineering and technology-based manufacturing
- attracting sound investment and talented people into engineering
- encouraging best practice in employee relations, health, safety and environmental management, and the recruitment, training and development of high calibre people
- encouraging higher standards of education and training in liaison with national strategic partners such as EMTA (the Engineering and Marine Training Authority).

EEF provides its members with a professional service which includes economic analysis and appropriate advisory services in employee relations; health, safety and environment; education and training; and employment law.

Engineering and Marine Training Authority

The Engineering and Marine Training Authority (EMTA) is appointed by the Department for Education and Employment as the National Training Organisation (NTO) for the Engineering Manufacture Sector, which includes Mechanical Engineering, Electrical Engineering, Electronics, Aerospace, Motor Vehicles and Shipbuilding.

As the NTO for engineering, EMTA represents the views and concerns of engineering employers to Government on education and training issues and is responsible for developing training systems such as Modern Apprenticeships, for the setting and maintenance of Occupational Standards for engineering, and for the promotion of training and human resource development, including Investors in People and Lifelong Learning.

EMTA also runs a careers service to help promote the image of engineering and to promote engineering as a career, particularly to young people. This includes running special initiatives to attract more women into engineering, such as the annual Insight programme for sixth-form girls run in conjunction with universities.

EMTA is also the leading Awarding Body for Engineering National Vocational Qualifications in England and Wales and Scottish Vocational Qualifications in Scotland.

The Wellcome Trust

The Wellcome Trust is the world's largest charity, spending some £250 million on medical research annually. The Trust supports more than 3000 researchers at 300 locations in 30 different countries laying the foundations for the healthcare advances of the next century and helping to maintain the UK's reputation as one of the world's leading scientific nations. As well as funding major initiatives in the public understanding of science, the Trust is the country's leading supporter of research into the history of medicine.

As a charity, the Wellcome Trust has always operated entirely independently of the Wellcome pharmaceutical company – a commercial operation that was known first as the Wellcome Foundation, then Wellcome plc. In 1995 Wellcome plc and Glaxo combined to form Glaxo Wellcome, in which the Wellcome Trust retains a 4.7 per cent interest.

WISE

The Engineering Council launched the Women Into Science and Engineering (WISE) campaign in 1984, jointly with the Equal Opportunities Commission, to encourage more women to consider careers in science and engineering. The campaign targets girls and women; parents; teaching staff in education and careers advisers; employers; politicians; and the media.

Booklets, posters and videos are available from the Engineering Council as well as a fleet of five vehicles converted into mobile technology classrooms, used in secondary schools to give girls an opportunity to sample technology.

To cater for the specific needs of women in Wales, Northern Ireland and Scotland, the Council has launched WISE committees in these countries. Various initiatives have developed with the support of local organisations and industry.

The number of women studying on engineering degree programmes has risen from 7 per cent in 1984 when the campaign started, to 14 per cent now. Considering that the initiatives were run at a difficult economic time, this progress is most encouraging.

Index

Profiles